SOLIDS: Elementary Theory for Advanced Students

SOLIDS: ELEMENTARY THEORY FOR ADVANCED STUDENTS

Gabriel Weinreich *Professor of Physics, University of Michigan*

John Wiley & Sons, Inc.   New York · London · Sydney

Library of Congress Catalog Card Number: 65-21431
Printed in the United States of America

to Bill Shockley

Preface

This book is addressed primarily to students of physics who have mastered the contents of standard courses in quantum mechanics, electromagnetic theory, and statistical physics such as are customarily presented in the first two years of graduate school, but who have had no background in the specific study of the solid state. Its purpose is to give the reader some feeling for what solid state physics is all about, rather than to cover any appreciable fraction of the huge territory which has come to be included under that title. For this reason I have chosen to treat a relatively small number of topics, but have tried to do it without the corner-cutting which is necessary when the amount of material is too large, or when the presentation is addressed to people who do not know enough physics.

The text is characterized by an almost complete absence of descriptive material having to do with actual properties of particular solids. A sufficiently naive reader might get the impression that no experiments on solids have ever been done; stubbornly refusing to read between the lines, he might even conclude that there is no need to do any, since whatever is of importance can be predicted *a priori*. It is, of course, typical of physical theory to stand as a proud and arrogant edifice, pretending that it could have been constructed without the much less elegant scaffolding of experimental observation. Whoever expects to become a solid-state physicist will naturally have to acquire a knowledge of empirical facts; but even he—and certainly those other physicists whose specialty is elsewhere, and whose interest in the solid state is primarily cultural—may appreciate a presentation in which the emphasis is on the logical cohesion of the theory rather than on its empirical basis.

The following are the reasons why I have decided against the inclusion of any bibliography. As regards textbooks, there are of course quite a number in this field, and I have always encouraged my students to browse actively through library shelves looking for treatments that appeal to *them*—rather than ask for *my* prejudices which are, after all, already amply expressed in my own presentation. On the other hand, the reason why I give no references of a purely factual, rather than pedagogical, nature is that one single reference suffices: Seitz and Turnbull, eds., *Solid State Physics*, Academic Press, New York. This monumental series of volumes (whose augmentation happily continues) contains treatments of so many topics, and leaves so few untouched upon, that together with its own bibliographies it serves as a sufficient gateway to the literature of the field.

Gabriel Weinreich

Ann Arbor
June 1965

Contents

Chapter 3   Vibration Spectrum of a Lattice

Chapter 4   Quantization of Lattice Vibrations
                 and Calculation of Specific Heat

Chapter 5   Interaction with Electromagnetic Radiation

SOLIDS: Elementary Theory for Advanced Students

1

The Geometrical Symmetry
of Crystal Structures

1.1 Introduction

The study of the solid state is to a large degree based on the spatial regularity of a crystal lattice. For this reason, it is important to develop first some of the mathematical properties which such a periodic lattice has. By way of comparison, we may note that the ordinary empty space ("the vacuum") in which the processes of mechanics proceed is characterized by the fact that *all points are equivalent*; the system under consideration if shifted by any amount in any direction would be capable of exactly the same type of behavior. It is well known that this invariance of the laws of mechanics against translations has as a consequence the law of conservation of momentum for closed systems; and that the corresponding invariance against rotations similarly leads to conservation of angular momentum.

Clearly, the mechanical system which we denote by the word "solid" also exists in the same vacuum, and the laws of conservation of *total* linear and angular momentum hold for it as well as for anything else. This is, however, beside the point, since we are ordinarily interested in studying the motion of some part of the system only, regarding the remainder as fixed. Whether this approach is justified by a weakness of coupling of various modes of motion (perturbation theory) or by a wide disparity between characteristic frequencies (adiabatic approximation), it remains in most cases the only method which presents any hope of obtaining reasonable solutions to the very complex problem in question.

Accordingly, if we are to study the motion of, say, a single electron in a crystal, we would not say that it moves in an environment which is invariant against arbitrary translations and rotations; in other words, neither the linear nor the angular momentum of an individual electron is a constant of the motion. In this chapter we shall discuss the *special* translations and rotations which do reproduce the lattice, giving rise to conservation laws which are characteristic of the crystalline structure.

1.2   Crystal Classes

A *macroscopic*[1] examination of a crystal would lead one to describe it as a homogeneous but anisotropic structure. If we took a large crystal of quartz, cut a plate out of it of some given dimensions, and examined its physical properties, we would find that two geometrically identical plates

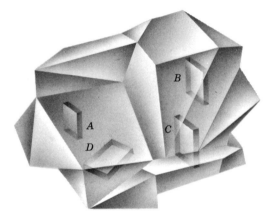

Fig. 1.1 Geometrically congruent crystal plates behave identically if their positions in the parent crystal are parallel to each other: plates *A*, *B*, *C* have the same properties, while those of *D* are in general different.

cut from two parts of the same crystal would behave identically provided their positions in the crystal were parallel to each other, that is, provided they differed by no more than a rigid translation. On the other hand, if the displacement which takes one plate into the other had a rotation component, their properties would in general be quite different (Fig. 1.1).

There is, of course, a limit as to how large a rigid translation within a crystal can be; this limit is set by how large the crystal is. Cursory examination shows, however, that the size of a crystal is not an "important"

---

[1] A "macroscopic" experiment is one which is incapable of resolving small distances. Optical experiments on crystals are macroscopic because the wavelength of light is large compared to the spacing of atoms; x-ray diffraction experiments are not, in spite of the size of the apparatus.

variable; crystals come in a wide range of sizes. If we cut our plate in some particular orientation and size, the only thing that can be concluded from its properties regarding the size of the original crystal is that it was at least as large as the plate. We may, therefore, imagine crystals to exist in any size we please; that very large ones may be technically hard to come by does not change the fact that no violence is done to the study of their properties by assuming their existence.

Accordingly, we temporarily eliminate from consideration rigid translations of a crystal as being "unimportant," and concentrate on the "point operations"; that is, the rigid displacements which leave one point of the crystal fixed. There are three types of point operations: rotations about an axis through the fixed point, reflections[2] in a plane through the fixed point, and combinations of the two.

It is in fact found that, for most crystals, there are some special point operations which *do* leave the properties of the crystal invariant. Thus, for quartz it is found that there exists a direction about which the crystal can be rotated by 120° without changing its properties in any way, and that there are three further directions about which a 180° rotation will give the same results. The list of all point operations which leave the macroscopic properties of a particular crystal invariant is called the *crystal class* (or *macroscopic point group*) of the crystal.[3] There exist exactly thirty-two different crystal classes; the reasons for this somewhat surprising fact will appear in the following sections.

1.3 Bravais Lattices and Crystal Structures

The previous section outlined a way of characterizing the symmetry of crystals which is natural from a macroscopic point of view. If, on the other hand, we were able to see a crystal on a scale of atomic dimensions (Fig. 1.2), we would probably be struck first by the regular spatial arrangements of the individual atoms. It now appears that the invariance of the structure under rigid translations has been overstated: a general translation does *not* reproduce the original crystal, even apart from boundary

[2] To test an object for reflection symmetry it is not, of course, necessary to push it with Alice through the looking-glass. One uses the same object, but constructs the *experimental equipment* in mirror image.

[3] "Point group" is a term for geometry, and means a set of operations which forms a group, i.e., has the property that any succession of operations in the set, viewed as a single operation, is also a member of the set. "Crystal class" is a term from physics, and means the point group which characterized the macroscopic properties of a crystal. The confusion between the two which exists in the literature is especially unfortunate in that point groups appear again in connection with microscopic symmetries (Sec. 1.8ff.).

considerations. Nevertheless, if we choose an arbitrary point P in the crystal structure, we can easily identify a large number of points P', P'', etc., which are *equivalent* to P; that is, the crystal looks the same from P as it does from any of the equivalent points. A translation vector such as PP', which *does* reproduce the structure (ignoring the boundaries, of course), is called a *lattice translation vector*. The set of lattice translation

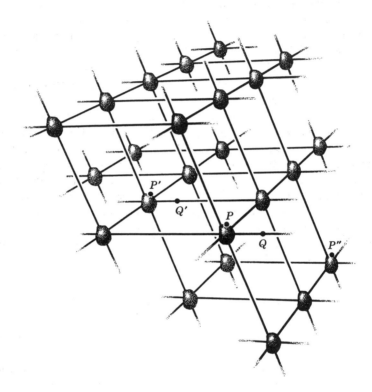

Fig. 1.2   Microscopic view of a crystal.

vectors is independent of the choice of P; a vector equal to PP' but originating at a point Q will terminate in a point Q' which is equivalent to Q. An arbitrary translation vector is not a lattice translation vector, but differs from one by a vector of atomic dimensions, which explains why macroscopically a crystal appears to be completely homogeneous.

The set of all points which are equivalent to each other form a pattern called a *Bravais lattice*. It is basically a mathematical entity, defined as a discrete set of points in three-dimensional space which looks the same viewed from one of its points as it does from any other; in other words, if a vector **R** starting on a point P_1 of the lattice terminates on a point P_2 of the lattice, then the same vector **R** starting on *any* point P_3 of the lattice will end on *some* point P_4 of the lattice.

A *crystal structure* is obtained if something (called the *basis* of the structure) is repeated through space in the pattern of a Bravais lattice. The Bravais lattice is, accordingly, the recipe for locating identical copies of the basis in space, whereas the basis is the thing an identical copy of which is placed at each point of the lattice. Of course, in a physical crystal the basis consists of some group of ions or atoms.[4]

1.4   Primitive Translation Vectors

For a given Bravais lattice, it is possible to find three vectors a_1, a_2, a_3 such that any lattice translation vector can be written in the form

$$\mathbf{R} = l\mathbf{a_1} + m\mathbf{a_2} + n\mathbf{a_3} \qquad (1.1)$$

where *l*, *m*, *n*, are integers. The required construction is as follows:

1. Choose as a_1 any lattice vector which is *the shortest one in its direction*.

Fig. 1.3   The first primitive vector generates a line of equally spaced points.

Because all points of the lattice are equivalent, such an a_1 will, applied to some point O of the lattice, generate a line of equally spaced points extending indefinitely in both directions (Fig. 1.3). This line clearly cannot contain any lattice points *not* generated by a_1's without violating the criterion by which a_1 was chosen. Moreover, *every* point in the whole lattice lies on an identical parallel line with identical spacing.

2. Find two such lines which in their common plane have no lattice points between them. Choose as a_2 any lattice vector which connects the two (Fig. 1.4).

---

[4] A crystal structure whose basis is a single atom is sometimes referred to as a "Bravais lattice," whereas a more complex structure is called a "lattice with a basis." This unfortunate nomenclature arises because in some problems the spatial extent of atoms is immaterial, the position of the (massive) nuclei being the only thing that counts.

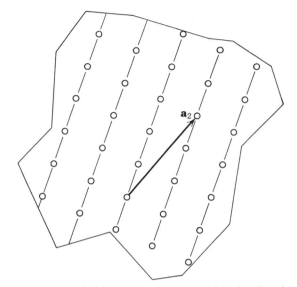

Fig. 1.4   The second primitive vector connects neighboring lines in a plane.

Successive applications of $\mathbf{a}_2$ generate a plane of points from a single line, and there are no lattice points in this plane which are not so generated. Furthermore, every point of the lattice lies on an identical parallel "$\mathbf{a}_1\mathbf{a}_2$-plane."

3. Find two such planes which have no lattice points lying between them. Choose as $\mathbf{a}_3$ any lattice vector which connects the two (Fig. 1.5).

To show that Eq. (1.1) is now satisfied, consider any two points P and Q of the lattice. If they are not in the same $\mathbf{a}_1\mathbf{a}_2$-plane, we can use some

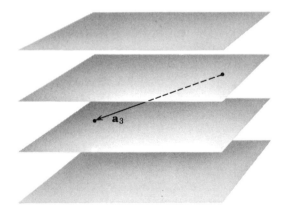

Fig. 1.5   The third primitive vector connects neighboring planes.

integral number of a_3's to go from P to somewhere in the plane of Q. From there we reach the "a_1-line" containing Q by successive applications of a_2, and finally, using a_1's we arrive at Q itself. Thus any lattice vector has the form of Eq. (1.1).

The three vectors a_1, a_2, and a_3 are called *primitive translation vectors* of the space lattice. The construction used in obtaining them shows that they are not unique; indeed, there is a great amount of freedom in how the set is chosen. The converse of the preceding theorem, namely, that any vector of the form (1.1) is a lattice translation vector, is obvious from the basic equivalence of all points of the lattice. It follows, incidentally, that a Bravais lattice has inversion symmetry about any lattice point.

The parallelepiped defined by a_1, a_2, a_3, whose volume is $a_1 \cdot a_2 \times a_3$, contains no points except at the corners. If we imagine the lattice built up of such parallelepipedal *primitive cells*, we see that eight cells would meet at each lattice point; since each cell has eight corners, the cell volume is equal to the volume per lattice point, and its reciprocal is the density of lattice points. Thus the triple product $a_1 \cdot a_2 \times a_3$ must be the same for any choice of primitive vectors.

From the point of view of translations alone, no Bravais lattice is more or less symmetrical than any other; indeed, any lattice can be transformed into any other by an affine transformation which changes the primitive vectors of the one into those of the other. In the next section we introduce operations that enable us to compare lengths of non-parallel vectors, which we have not heretofore been called upon to do. New symmetries will appear as a result.

1.5 Rotational Symmetry of a Bravais Lattice

A *rotation axis* of a Bravais lattice is a line such that the lattice is unchanged after rotation about it of some angle. (If a rotation axis is translated by a lattice translation vector, it is clearly still a rotation axis; two such axes are said to be *equivalent*). Since the lattice consists of discrete points, each axis must be characterized by a finite minimum rotation angle, which we shall call φ_0. Any other angle ψ which represents a symmetry rotation about the same axis has to be an integral multiple of φ_0; for the double inequality

$$\frac{\psi}{\varphi_0} \leqslant \nu < \frac{\psi}{\varphi_0} + 1 \tag{1.2}$$

uniquely defines an integer ν, which in turn also satisfies

$$0 \leqslant \nu\varphi_0 - \psi < \varphi_0. \tag{1.3}$$

But since φ_0 and ψ are both allowed rotations, $\nu\varphi_0 - \psi$ is also allowed. Therefore, the equality sign on the left side of Eq. (1.3) must hold, otherwise the assumption that φ_0 is the smallest allowed rotation angle would be contradicted.

Obviously, every rotation axis has 360° as an allowed rotation angle; it follows that φ_0 must be an integral submultiple of 360°. The term "n-fold axis" is used to denote an axis for which the ratio $(360°/\varphi_0)$ is equal to n.

The translational symmetry of a Bravais lattice has as a consequence that n is limited to the values 2, 3, 4, or 6. To see the reason for this limitation, consider some lattice plane perpendicular to the axis in question (Fig. 1.6). Let O be the point where the axis pierces this plane (not necessarily a lattice point); let P be a lattice point in the plane such that no

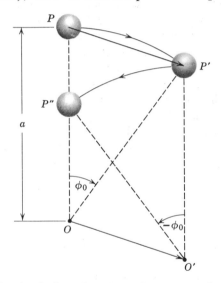

Fig. 1.6 Construction for finding allowed rotation angles: P'' must either coincide with O, or be at least as far from O as P is.

other point is closer to O than P is (this is a valid construction, since we know the lattice to be discrete). Let a be the distance OP.

Now perform a rotation through φ_0, the smallest allowed angle, so that point P is taken into point P'. Since the vector PP' is thus shown to be a lattice vector, it follows that there is another equivalent rotation axis piercing the plane at a point O' displaced from O by the vector PP'. Let the rotation around O' through the angle $-\varphi_0$ take P' into P''.

Simple geometry shows that P'' lies on the line OP a distance $2a(1 - \cos \varphi_0)$ from P toward O. But by construction P'' cannot be closer to O than P is, unless P'' coincides with O. Therefore, either $2a[1 - \cos(2\pi/n)] \geqslant 2a$, which means that $n = 2$, 3, or 4; or else $2a[1 - \cos(2\pi/n)] = a$, which means that $n = 6$. The latter case requires, of course, that *every* lattice plane perpendicular to the axis contain a point *on* the axis.

A plane perpendicular to a rotation axis and containing one lattice point contains an infinite two-dimensional net of points, so that the whole lattice can be constructed by stacking such nets on top of each other. To

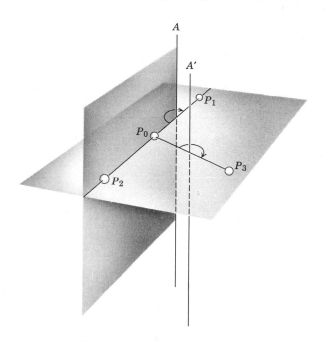

Fig. 1.7 A plane perpendicular to a two-fold axis and containing a lattice point P_0 must contain an infinite net of points.

prove this statement if suffices to show that the plane contains at least three non-colinear points, which in turn is obvious if the axis has $n > 2$; for then the rotation itself produces, from the original point, at least two others. If the axis is only two-fold, the argument does not work, since we only get two distinct points P_0 and P_1, plus an infinity of other points like P_2 colinear with the first two (Fig. 1.7). However, since the primitive vectors are non-coplanar, at least one of them can be used to translate the original axis A out of the plane $AP_0P_1P_2$ to an equivalent axis A'. A rotation about the new axis then turns P_0 into P_3, a point outside the $P_0P_1P_2$ line.

The lattice planes perpendicular to a rotation axis, whose existence has just been proven, must themselves have rotational symmetry, since the axis takes any lattice point into another lying in the same plane. We are, therefore, led to examine the rotational symmetry of such "Bravais nets," before stacking them into the various possible three-dimensional lattices.

1.6 Plane Nets

The net of least possible symmetry is generated by two primitive vectors whose lengths and directions are unrelated, as shown in Fig. 1.8. This "oblique" net already has *four* nonequivalent two-fold axes: one through the lattice points (A), one through the parallelogram centers (B), and one each through the centers of the two parallelogram edges (C and D). Note, however, that the distinction between B, C, and D depends on the choice of the primitive cells; Fig. 1.8 shows an alternative (dashed) parallelogram with respect to which C, rather than B, is at the center. It is,

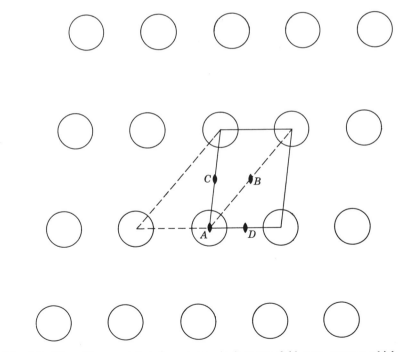

Fig. 1.8 The oblique net has four nonequivalent two-fold axes, among which two types can be distinguished independently of the choice of primitive vectors.

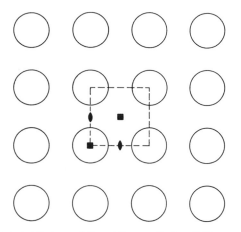

Fig. 1.9   In the square net, two of the oblique net's two-fold axes become four-fold.

therefore, more relevant to say that the oblique net contains *two types* of axes: those that go through lattice points and those that do not.

It is shown in Problem 2 at the end of this chapter that a net which has an n-fold axis anywhere must also have an n-fold axis through its lattice points. Thus a net with four-fold symmetry has four-fold symmetry about its lattice points and a net with six-fold symmetry has six-fold symmetry about its lattice points. Figure 1.9 and 1.10, respectively, show these two two-dimensional lattices. Note that the "square" net has an additional four-fold axis through the centers of the square cells. A net with a three-fold axis anywhere combines at its lattice points the three-fold axis required by Problem 2 with the two-fold axis which a plane net has automatically, so that it actually has a six-fold axis there and is, in fact, the same net as in Fig. 1.10.

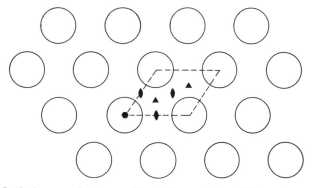

Fig. 1.10   In the hexagonal net, one of the oblique net's two-fold axes becomes six-fold; in addition, two three-fold axes appear.

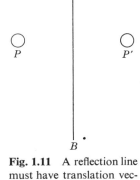

Fig. 1.11 A reflection line must have translation vectors perpendicular to it.

This completes the classification of nets by perpendicular rotation axes. In general, an axis which is not perpendicular to the net cannot turn the net into itself, but to this rule there exists the important exception of a two-fold axis in the plane of the net, which acts as a *reflection line* within the net.

In Fig. 1.11, let AB be a reflection line, and P a lattice point in the plane. The reflection operation then produces the lattice point P', showing that there exist lattice translation vectors perpendicular to AB. According to Section 1.4, it is then possible to choose the primitive translation $\mathbf{a}_1$ perpendicular to AB, so that the whole net must consist of identical lines perpendicular to AB, with the points on each line equally spaced. Such a line has two possible nonequivalent reflection points: the lattice points themselves and the midpoints between them. Starting with one line, the next one can, therefore, be placed in one of two ways so as to maintain the reflection symmetry, and since the position of all other lines is then fixed, there are two possible plane nets which exhibit reflection symmetry. These are the rectangular and rhombic nets, shown in Figs. 1.12 and 1.13.

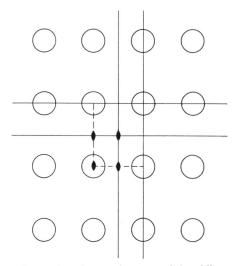

Fig. 1.12 The rectangular net has the rotation axes of the oblique net plus four non-equivalent reflection lines.

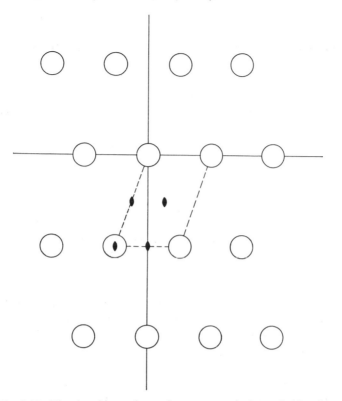

Fig. 1.13   The rhombic net has only two nonequivalent reflection lines.

1.7   Organization of Lattices by Crystal Systems

We are now ready to classify the three-dimensional Bravais lattices by the *crystal system* to which they belong, that is, by the type of rotational axes which they possess. There are altogether seven crystal systems, which we shall now investigate in order.

Triclinic System. A lattice is completely determined by de-cribing one crystal plane and specifying how the next plane above it (which must be identical) is placed in relation to it. Now each of the plane nets we have discussed has two-fold symmetry axes; if we do not want the lattice as a whole to have this symmetry, we need merely stagger the next plane above so that these axes do not coincide. This produces the *triclinic lattice*—the only member of the triclinic system. There is, of course, no reason here why the individual planes should have any special symmetry; they will presumably have the appearance of Fig. 1.8, though, of course, they could be *approximately* square, triangular, etc., for accidental reasons.

Monoclinic System. If we do want to preserve the two-fold axis for the whole lattice, we again start with the oblique net of Fig. 1.8, and place the next plane so that its points are either directly above the points of the first plane, or directly above one of the points *B*, *C*, or *D*. The first produces the *simple monoclinic lattice*; the second, the *centered monoclinic lattice*.

Trigonal System. The requirement here is the existence of a three-fold axis, so that we must start with the hexagonal net of Fig. 1.10, which has a three-fold axis through the triangle centers and a six-fold axis through the lattice points. Since we do not want the lattice as a whole to have a six-fold axis, we are forced to place the next plane so that the triangle centers are directly above the lattice points of the first plane. The resulting arrangement is called the *rhombohedral* lattice, and is the only member of the trigonal system.

Tetragonal System. This time we require a four-fold axis to exist. Starting, as we must, with the square lattice, we have two choices closely analogous to those for the monoclinic system. As a result we get the *simple tetragonal* and the *centered tetragonal* lattices.

Hexagonal System. From the discussion of the trigonal system, it is clear that there is one and only one way of constructing a lattice with a six-fold axis. It is called simply the *hexagonal lattice*.

Orthorhombic System. Here there are two two-fold axes perpendicular to each other. Clearly, we can construct lattices of the orthorhombic system by starting with either the rectangular or the rhombic net and following one of the two recipes used in making up the monoclinic lattices. As a result we have four lattices, called *simple* orthorhombic, *body-centered* orthorhombic, *base-centered* orthorhombic, and *face-centered* orthorhombic.

Cubic System. This system has two four-fold axes perpendicular to each other. In this case we start with the tetragonal lattices and add the additional symmetry requirement. A four-fold axis parallel to the sides of the square nets making up the planes of the simple tetragonal lattice converts it into the simple cubic. The same modification of the centered tetragonal produces the body-centered cubic; whereas placing the new four-fold axis at forty-five degrees to the first choice changes the centered tetragonal into the face-centered cubic lattice.

The fourteen Bravais lattices which thus finally emerge are shown in Fig. 1.14. Note that the difference between simple, body-centered, base-centered, and face-centered lattices depends on rotational rather than translational symmetry. For example, the triclinic lattice, which we usually

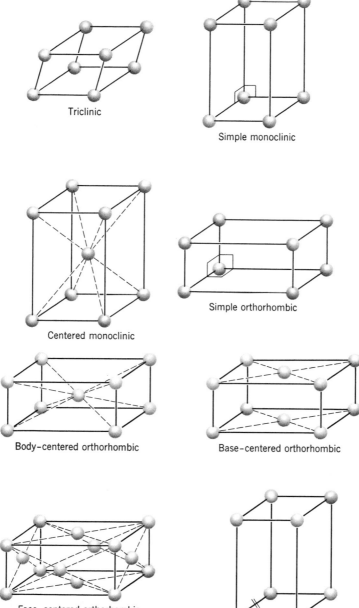

Fig. 1.14   The fourteen Bravais lattices.

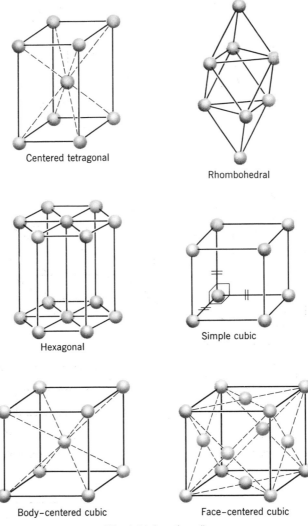

Centered tetragonal

Rhombohedral

Hexagonal

Simple cubic

Body-centered cubic

Face-centered cubic

Fig. 1.14 (continued)

think of as simple, can be equally well represented by a unit cell[5] which is centered in any one of the three possible ways, as shown in Fig. 1.15; there is no way, however, to make this distinction meaningful. On the other hand, the two monoclinic lattices differ in that one (the "simple" one) has two kinds of two-fold axes, one of which goes through a point

[5] A *unit cell* is one which can generate the lattice by translation; it differs from the primitive cell in not being necessarily the smallest such unit.

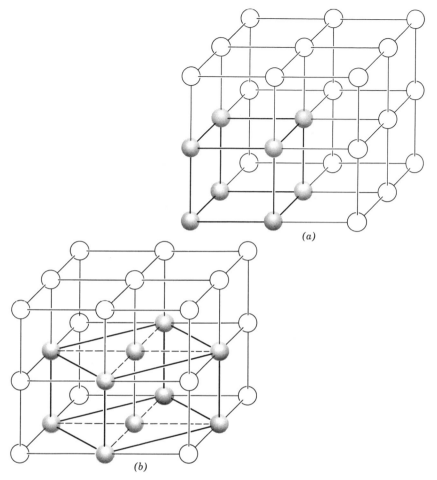

Fig. 1.15 The triclinic lattice can be equally well thought of as simple (*a*), base-centered (*b*), body-centered (*c*), or face-centered (*d*).

in every plane, while the other goes through no points; whereas every two-fold axis of the "centered monoclinic" goes through a point in every other plane. Figure 1.16 shows five monoclinic cells which are respectively simple, body-centered, rectangle-centered, parallelogram-centered, and face-centered.[6] Applying the criterion just mentioned, we find that the first and fourth are the same lattice, as are the second, third, and fifth.

---

[6] In the figure the two-fold axis is taken as vertical, which happens to disagree with a crystallographic convention. Crystallography, like every well-established discipline, has a certain number of arbitrary conventions which the experts take for granted, but which an outsider must check carefully.

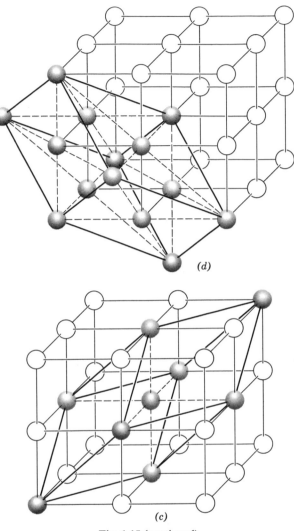

(d)

(c)

Fig. 1.15 (continued)

Indeed, Fig. 1.16 shows the construction by which the parallelogram-centered cell becomes explicitly simple; the corresponding reduction of the rectangle-centered and face-centered cells to body-centered is indicated in Fig. 1.17.

As in the case of the orthorhombic lattices, where the existence of two two-fold axes implies the existence of a third, all the lattices actually contain more symmetry than is required for their definition.

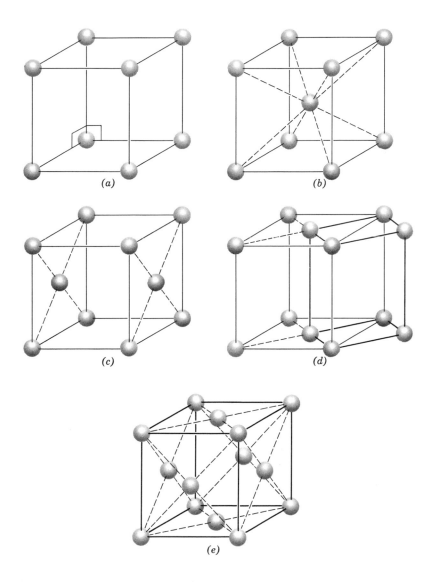

Fig. 1.16 Of the five conceivable monoclinic lattices [(*a*) simple; (*b*) body-centered; (*c*) rectangle-centered; (*d*) parallelogram-centered; and (*e*) face-centered] only two can be meaningfully distinguished. Thus (*d*) is equivalent to (*a*), as the heavy construction lines show.

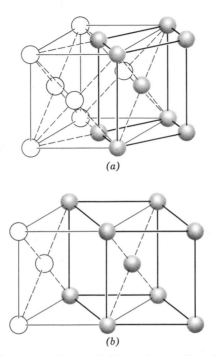

(a)

(b)

Fig. 1.17   (*a*) The "face-centered monoclinic" can be equally well thought of as body-centered, as can the "rectangle-centered monoclinic" (*b*).

1.8   Point Symmetry of the Basis

The intuitively obvious fact that the point symmetry of the basis of a crystal structure is closely related to that of its Bravais lattice is a consequence of physics; mathematically, there is nothing to preclude the arrangement of perfect spheres in a triclinic lattice, or of irregular (but, of course, identical) potatoes in a cubic lattice. Physically, however, the atom or cluster of atoms which comprises the basis will be distorted by forces exerted by the atoms on other sites, so that any symmetry element which the basis has must also be a symmetry element of the Bravais lattice.[7]

Conversely, the lattice of a physical crystal is held in its particular configuration by interatomic forces, and any symmetry which the lattice

[7] When we speak of the point symmetry of the basis we mean the symmetry in the actual crystal structure. Sodium, for example, is a spherically symmetric atom when it is isolated; but in its (body-centered cubic) crystal structure it becomes distorted to cubic symmetry.

has must be somehow due to symmetry of those forces. Consider, for example, a monoclinic lattice: its point group has two elements, namely a two-fold rotation axis and a reflection plane perpendicular to it, which a triclinic lattice lacks. If a certain crystal is monoclinic and we ask why it does not distort to triclinic, the answer can only be that the interatomic pattern of forces, and hence the basis, has at least one of these symmetry elements. It need not, of course, have both, for it is impossible for the lattice to lose one without the other.

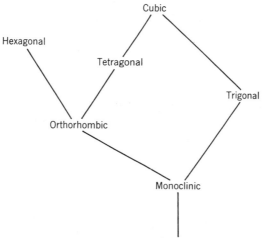

Fig. 1.18 Hierarchy of crystal systems: every system is a special case of the ones below it.

Accordingly, we can sum up the limitations on the symmetry of the basis in the following two rules:

a. the basis can have *no* symmetry element not possessed by the lattice;

b. the basis must have *at least one* symmetry element not possessed by any lattice which can be obtained from the actual one by an infinitesimal distortion.

A systematic enumeration of the point groups which can possibly characterize the basis of a crystal structure begins with the hierarchy of systems shown in Fig. 1.18. In this diagram every system can be produced from the one above it by an infinitesimal distortion; conversely, every system can be considered to be a special case of the one below it. Thus, a cubic lattice becomes trigonal (i.e., rhombohedral) when it is pulled out (or pushed in) along a body diagonal, whereas it becomes tetragonal when pulled along an edge. Similarly, a hexagonal lattice can be viewed as a

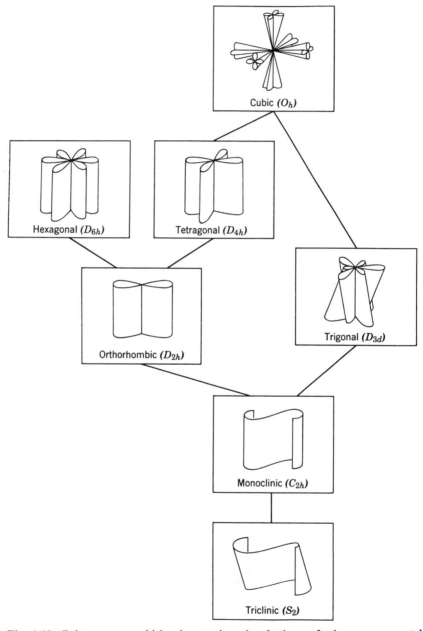

Fig. 1.19 Point groups which characterize the lattices of the seven crystal systems.

base-centered orthorhombic one having the sides of the centered rectangle in a ratio of $\sqrt{3}:1$; the base-centered orthorhombic is in turn a simple monoclinic whose base parallelogram is equilateral; and so on.

The two preceding rules can now be embodied in the following statement: *the point group of the basis of a crystal structure must be a subgroup*[8] *of the point group of its lattice, but not a subgroup of the point group of any lattice which is below it in the hierarchy.*

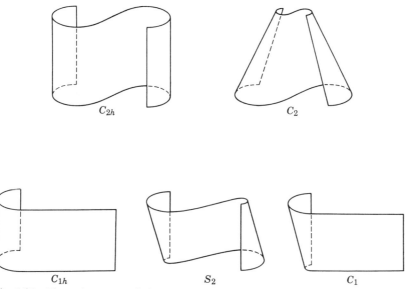

Fig. 1.20   The point group of the monoclinic lattice has five subgroups, of which the last two belong to the triclinic system.

The seven point groups characterizing the lattices of the crystal systems are represented in Fig. 1.19 by objects which have the corresponding symmetry; the elements of each group can be enumerated by (careful) inspection. For example, the monoclinic lattice has the previously mentioned two-fold axis and horizontal reflection plane, as well as the inversion; the triclinic lattice has the inversion only.

Figure 1.20 shows all the subgroups of the monoclinic group. Clearly, only the first three belong to the monoclinic system; the last two are subgroups of the triclinic point group. We conclude that there are three possible symmetry groups which the basis of a monoclinic crystal structure can have, and that similarly two possibilities exist for a triclinic structure. Figure 1.21 shows the result of the same process carried out for all systems.

[8] A subgroup is a group (cf. note 3 on p. 3) all of whose elements are also members of the original group. As used here, a group is to be included as one of its own subgroups.

Triclinic:

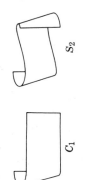

C_1 S_2

Monoclinic:

C_{1h}

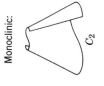

C_2

C_{2h}

Orthorhombic:

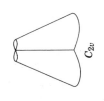

C_{2v} D_2

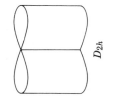

D_{2h}

Tetragonal:

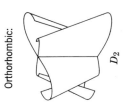

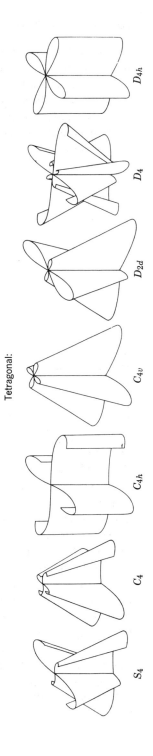

S_4 C_4 C_{4h} C_{4v} D_{2d} D_4 D_{4h}

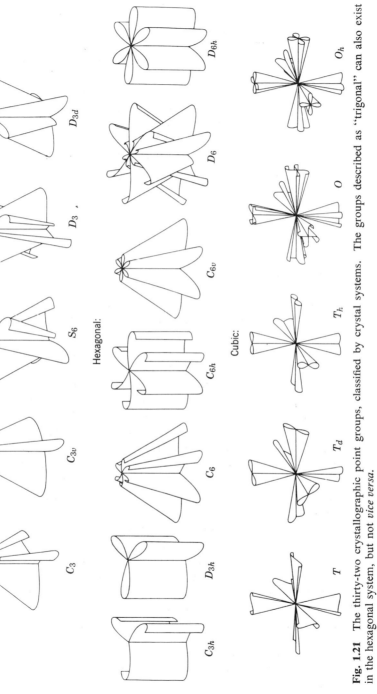

Trigonal:

C_3 C_{3v} S_6 D_3 D_{3d}

Hexagonal:

C_{3h} D_{3h} C_6 C_{6h} C_{6v} D_6 D_{6h}

Cubic:

T T_d T_h O O_h

Fig. 1.21 The thirty-two crystallographic point groups, classified by crystal systems. The groups described as "trigonal" can also exist in the hexagonal system, but not *vice versa*.

25

A rather special relation exists between the trigonal and hexagonal systems because of the fact that whereas the trigonal lattice point group is a subgroup of the hexagonal one, the trigonal (i.e., rhombohedral) lattice *cannot* be produced from the hexagonal one by an infinitesimal distortion. In fact, since all five trigonal point groups have a three-fold axis, which the systems below the hexagonal one in the hierarchy do not have, the trigonal groups can also characterize the basis of hexagonal structures! For this reason, it has sometimes been suggested that the rhombohedral and hexagonal lattices be considered to belong to a single hexagonal system. Against such a convention one might argue, first, that the seven "true hexagonal" point groups can exist *only* in the hexagonal lattice[9]; second, that the two lattices have different point symmetries. A settlement on six-and-a-half crystal systems seems to be the only equitable one.

1.9   Space Groups

The *space group* of a crystal structure is the group of all operations—translations, point operations, and combinations of the two—which leave the structure invariant. Since the Bravais lattice never has less point symmetry than the basis, the point group of the basis is also the point group of the crystal structure. The translation group of the structure, on the other hand, is that of the Bravais lattice. One might therefore suppose that any space group can be considered simply as a combination of a particular Bravais lattice with a point group belonging to the same system. Such a count would give, for example, fifteen cubic space groups, since the cubic system contains three lattices and five point groups. If we multiply the number of lattices by the number of point groups for each system and add, we obtain a total of sixty-six space groups; in fact, however, two hundred thirty separate space groups exist, for reasons which we must now investigate.

The space groups we were constructing in the previous paragraph are characterized by the fact that the basis can be diminished in size relative to the lattice spacing without upsetting any of the symmetry. They are called *symmorphic* space groups. Actually, there are seventy-three symmorphic space groups, seven more than in our previous count; the additions come from the fact that in a few cases there are two ways of orienting the point group relative to the lattice. As an example, consider

---

[9] They each contain at least one element—either a six-fold axis or a horizontal reflection plane—which the rhombohedral lattice does not have.

the cluster of four identical atoms shown in Fig. 1.22; its point group is D_{2d} and it, therefore, belongs to the tetragonal system. Now the tetragonal lattices have at their lattice points four horizontal two-fold axes and four vertical reflection planes, while D_{2d} has two two-fold axes *alternating* with two vertical reflection planes. Figure 1.23 shows how, as a result, two separate symmorphic space groups can be constructed using the same (simple) lattice and the same basis.

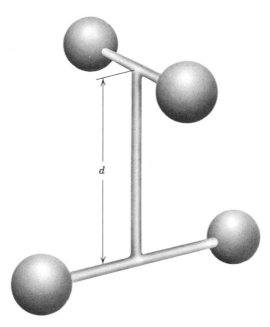

Fig. 1.22   The tetragonal point group D_{2d} has two horizontal two-fold axes alternating with two vertical reflection planes.

The same structures can also illustrate the origin of the non-symmorphic groups. Let d be the "size" of the basis (Fig. 1.22), and c the vertical lattice spacing in Fig. 1.23. If d is made equal to zero, the point group becomes D_{4h}; although the space group thereby changes, the resulting group is still one of the seventy-three symmorphic ones. Suppose, however, that we make d equal to $c/2$, as in Fig. 1.24. A new symmetry element then appears; namely, *a four-fold rotation about the vertical axis combined with a translation of half a lattice spacing* brings the crystal structure into itself. Such an element is called a *screw axis*. It is clear that this type of symmetry can appear only as a result of some special relationship between the scales of the lattice and the basis, and that the space groups which contain it

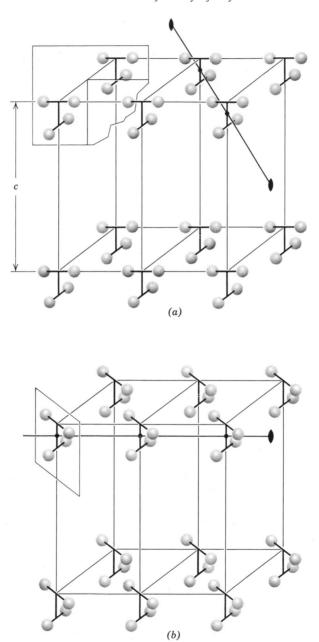

(a)

(b)

Fig. 1.23 Even in a symmorphic way, there are two distinct ways of combining the D_{2d} point group with the simple tetragonal lattice. In each case, a two-fold axis and a reflection plane are shown.

cannot be defined as elementary combinations of a Bravais lattice with a point group.

Although it is beyond our scope to give a more detailed description of the space groups, it should be mentioned that they may contain another type of symmetry element which, like the screw axis, is "mixed"; that is, it is a combination of a point operation with a translation such that neither one alone leaves the lattice invariant. The element in question is called

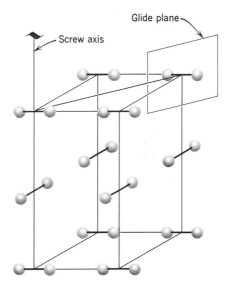

Glide plane

Screw axis

Fig. 1.24 A nonsymmorphic space group results from Fig. 1.23*a* by adjusting the dimensions of the basis relative to the spacing of the lattice. A screw axis and a glide plane are shown.

a *glide plane*, and consists of a reflection in a plane followed by a translation parallel to the plane. Figure 1.24 shows a glide plane whose translation is half a lattice spacing along the tetragonal axis.

If the space group of a crystal structure is symmorphic, then its crystal class will simply be the point group of its basis. On the other hand, screw axes and glide planes appear as rotation axes and reflection planes in the crystal class; for the difference between, say, a glide plane and a reflection plane is precisely the kind of microscopic translation which the crystal class ignores.

Accordingly, the two structures obtained from Fig. 1.23 by making d equal to $c/2$ belong to the crystal class D_{4h}; the same is true of the two corresponding ones based on the centered tetragonal lattice. In addition, there are two symmorphic D_{4h} space groups, one based on each lattice, so that the crystal class D_{4h} comprises at least six space groups. In actual fact, one finds (with the help of much geometry and patience) that there are twenty distinct space groups belonging to this class and, as we previously mentioned, two hundred thirty space groups altogether.

PROBLEMS

1. Construct two different sets of primitive translation vectors for the simple cubic lattice. Verify explicitly that the volume $\mathbf{a}_1 \cdot \mathbf{a}_2 \times \mathbf{a}_3$ is the same for both.

2. Prove that a Bravais net which has an n-fold axis anywhere must have an n-fold axis through its lattice points.

3. Prove that if a Bravais lattice has a reflection plane, it is possible to choose one primitive vector perpendicular to the plane and the two others parallel to it. Is this choice unique?

4. (*a*) A crystal structure has, as one if its symmetry elements, a reflection in a plane combined with a translation *not* parallel to the plane. Show that this is equivalent to an ordinary mirror plane, or a glide plane, in a different position, so that nothing new is introduced by considering such a symmetry element.

(*b*) Give the corresponding argument for a symmetry element consisting of a rotation followed by a translation *not* along the axis (it must be equivalent either to an ordinary rotation axis or a screw axis).

2

Waves in Lattices

2.1 Introduction

A good deal of the material of solid state physics concerns itself with various wave fields in the geometrical environment of a crystal structure. As examples we may quote electromagnetic fields, quantum-mechanical electron waves, waves of crystal vibration consisting of motion of the constituent atoms, and so on. It is, therefore, convenient to develop some aspects of wave formalism in general terms before applying this material to specific cases.

The crystal structure is, as we have seen, constructed from identical primitive cells. Since each of these is associated with a particular lattice point, we may label them by the lattice translation vector $\mathbf{R}$ which locates this point relative to some fiduciary lattice point taken as origin. The first question to ask about a particular field is then how many degrees of freedom it has per primitive cell. For the Schrödinger field this number is infinite; to specify it completely, the wave function has to be given for each point in the cell. On the other hand, the lattice vibration field, if we consider the atoms as points, has degrees of freedom per cell equal to three times the number of atoms per cell.

In general we specify the total field by some function $\xi(\sigma; \mathbf{R})$ in which $\mathbf{R}$ denotes which primitive cell we are in and σ runs through a number of values (finite or infinite) equal to the number of degrees of freedom per cell. In looking for the normal modes of propagation of the field, we are typically led to an eigenvalue problem of the form

$$\Omega \xi(\sigma; \mathbf{R}) = \lambda \xi(\sigma; \mathbf{R}) \tag{2.1}$$

where Ω is some linear operator. In general, there are no solutions

31

satisfying appropriate boundary conditions for arbitrary λ; the allowed values of λ are called *eigenvalues* of Ω, and the corresponding solutions $\xi_\lambda(\sigma; \mathbf{R})$ *eigenfunctions*. We now proceed to investigate what general conclusions can be drawn about these quantities as a result of our knowledge of the periodic environment.

2.2   Translation Operators

For each lattice translation vector $\mathbf{R}_i$ we define a translation operator $\mathscr{T}(\mathbf{R}_i)$ by

$$\mathscr{T}(\mathbf{R}_i)\xi(\sigma; \mathbf{R}) \equiv \xi(\sigma; \mathbf{R} + \mathbf{R}_i), \tag{2.2}$$

where ξ is any function of the type considered in the previous section. Clearly $\mathbf{R} + \mathbf{R}_i$ is also a lattice vector, so that the right side of Eq. (2.2) is well defined. Applying two such operators in succession, we obtain

$$\mathscr{T}(\mathbf{R}_2)\mathscr{T}(\mathbf{R}_1)\xi(\sigma; \mathbf{R}) = \mathscr{T}(\mathbf{R}_2)\xi(\sigma; \mathbf{R} + \mathbf{R}_1)$$

$$= \xi(\sigma; \mathbf{R} + \mathbf{R}_1 + \mathbf{R}_2) = \mathscr{T}(\mathbf{R}_1)\mathscr{T}(\mathbf{R}_2)\xi(\sigma; \mathbf{R}).$$

$$\tag{2.3}$$

Since ξ in Eq. (2.3) was arbitrary we conclude that *any two translation operators commute*.

Consider now the "dynamical operator" Ω of Eq. (2.1). Since the lattice is assumed completely periodic (and hence infinite) in all directions, Ω cannot in any way discriminate among different absolute positions of primitive cells. If a lattice translation operator is applied to the function $\Omega\xi(\sigma; \mathbf{R})$, the result must, therefore, be the same as one would get by first translating ξ and then applying Ω; or

$$\mathscr{T}(\mathbf{R}_1)\Omega\xi(\sigma; \mathbf{R}) = \Omega\mathscr{T}(\mathbf{R}_1)\xi(\sigma; \mathbf{R}) \tag{2.4}$$

for any ξ and any $\mathscr{T}$. This shows that Ω commutes with all the $\mathscr{T}$'s of the lattice.

We now invoke the theorem that if all operators of a set commute in pairs, the eigenfunctions of one can be so constructed as to be simultaneous eigenfunctions of all. Accordingly, we look for solutions of the eigenvalue problem, Eq. (2.1), which are at the same time simultaneous eigenfunctions of all the translation operators of the lattice.

2.3   Eigenfunctions of the Translation Operators

Consider a function $\xi(\sigma; \mathbf{R})$ which is a simultaneous eigenfunction of all translation operators. By definition this means that for each translation $\mathscr{T}(\mathbf{R}_1)$ there exists a number $C(\mathbf{R}_1)$ such that

$$\mathscr{T}(\mathbf{R}_1)\xi(\sigma; \mathbf{R}) \equiv \xi(\sigma; \mathbf{R} + \mathbf{R}_1) = C(\mathbf{R}_1)\xi(\sigma; \mathbf{R}). \tag{2.5}$$

Let $\mathscr{T}(\mathbf{R}_1)$ and $\mathscr{T}(\mathbf{R}_2)$ be any two translation operators; then

$$\mathscr{T}(\mathbf{R}_2)\mathscr{T}(\mathbf{R}_1)\xi(\sigma; \mathbf{R}) = C(\mathbf{R}_2)C(\mathbf{R}_1)\xi(\sigma; \mathbf{R}). \tag{2.6}$$

But the product $\mathscr{T}(\mathbf{R}_2)\mathscr{T}(\mathbf{R}_1)$ is itself a lattice translation operator $\mathscr{T}(\mathbf{R}_2 + \mathbf{R}_1)$, so that

$$\mathscr{T}(\mathbf{R}_2 + \mathbf{R}_1)\xi(\sigma; \mathbf{R}) = C(\mathbf{R}_2 + \mathbf{R}_1)\xi(\sigma; \mathbf{R}); \tag{2.7}$$

hence $\qquad\qquad C(\mathbf{R}_2 + \mathbf{R}_1) = C(\mathbf{R}_2)C(\mathbf{R}_1) \tag{2.8}$

for any $\mathbf{R}_1$, $\mathbf{R}_2$. Therefore, the numbers $C(\mathbf{R})$ must depend exponentially on $\mathbf{R}$:

$$C(\mathbf{R}) = e^{\mu \cdot \mathbf{R}} \tag{2.9}$$

where the vector μ characterizes the particular ξ. Note however that, since Eq. (2.9) implies that

$$\xi(\sigma; \mathbf{R}) = e^{\mu \cdot \mathbf{R}}\xi(\sigma; \mathbf{0}), \tag{2.10}$$

we would in general have the function ξ growing exponentially larger and larger in some directions. As long as the crystal is considered infinite, such behavior is not admissible. Therefore μ must of the form $i\mathbf{k}$, where $\mathbf{k}$ is a real vector.

Finally, denoting $\xi(\sigma; \mathbf{0})$ simply by $\xi(\sigma)$, we arrive at

Theorem 1.   A simultaneous eigenfunction of all translation operators satisfying the boundary conditions for an infinite crystal must be of the form

$$\xi(\sigma)e^{i\mathbf{k} \cdot \mathbf{R}}. \tag{2.11}$$

Corollary.   The solutions of the dynamical problem (2.1) can be written in the same form.

2.4   Reciprocal Lattice

The vector $\mathbf{k}$, through the function $e^{i\mathbf{k} \cdot \mathbf{R}}$, specifies the eigenvalues of all the translation operators corresponding to a particular eigenfunction $\xi_\mathbf{k}$.

Some redundancy exists, however, because of the fact that $\mathbf{R}$ takes discrete values only. Thus if a vector $\mathbf{K}$ can be found such that

$$\mathbf{K} \cdot \mathbf{R} = 2\pi\nu, \tag{2.12}$$

where ν is integral for all $\mathbf{R}$, then

$$e^{i(\mathbf{k}+\mathbf{K}) \cdot \mathbf{R}} = e^{i\mathbf{k} \cdot \mathbf{R}} e^{2\pi i\nu} = e^{i\mathbf{k} \cdot \mathbf{R}}, \tag{2.13}$$

so that replacing $\mathbf{k}$ by $\mathbf{k} + \mathbf{K}$ gives the same eigenvalues for all translation operators. In other words, the set $\xi_{\mathbf{k}}$ of solutions of the dynamical problem is the same as the set of solutions $\xi_{\mathbf{k}+\mathbf{K}}$.

Let us, therefore, investigate what vectors $\mathbf{K}$ there are which satisfy Eq. 2.12. Starting with the primitive lattice translation vectors, define

$$\mathbf{b}^1 \equiv \frac{2\pi\mathbf{a}_2 \times \mathbf{a}_3}{\mathbf{a}_1 \cdot \mathbf{a}_2 \times \mathbf{a}_3}$$

$$\mathbf{b}^2 \equiv \frac{2\pi\mathbf{a}_3 \times \mathbf{a}_1}{\mathbf{a}_1 \cdot \mathbf{a}_2 \times \mathbf{a}_3} \tag{2.14}$$

$$\mathbf{b}^3 \equiv \frac{2\pi\mathbf{a}_1 \times \mathbf{a}_2}{\mathbf{a}_1 \cdot \mathbf{a}_2 \times \mathbf{a}_3};$$

these new vectors have the property

$$\mathbf{a}_i \cdot \mathbf{b}^j = 2\pi\delta_{ij}, \tag{2.15}$$

which is easily verified. The vectors $\mathbf{K}_{LMN}$ defined for integer values of L, M, and N by

$$\mathbf{K}_{LMN} \equiv L\mathbf{b}^1 + M\mathbf{b}^2 + N\mathbf{b}^3 \tag{2.16}$$

are called *reciprocal lattice vectors*; the set defines a new lattice called the *reciprocal lattice*. We can now prove two theorems which will answer the question of the redundancy in specifying $\mathbf{k}$-values of eigenfunctions.

Theorem 2. If $\mathbf{K}$ is any reciprocal lattice vector and $\mathbf{R}$ any direct[1] lattice vector, then the scalar product $\mathbf{K} \cdot \mathbf{R}$ is an integral multiple of 2π. PROOF. From Eqs. (1.1) and (2.16),

$$\mathbf{K} \cdot \mathbf{R} = (L\mathbf{b}^1 + M\mathbf{b}^2 + N\mathbf{b}^3) \cdot (l\mathbf{a}_1 + m\mathbf{a}_2 + n\mathbf{a}_3) \tag{2.17}$$

so that, due to Eq. (2.15),

$$\mathbf{K} \cdot \mathbf{R} = (Ll + Mm + Nn)2\pi. \tag{2.18}$$

Theorem 3. If for some vector $\mathbf{K}$ the scalar product $\mathbf{K} \cdot \mathbf{R}$ is an integral multiple of 2π for all lattice vectors $\mathbf{R}$, then $\mathbf{K}$ is a vector of the reciprocal lattice.

[1] The "direct lattice" is the ordinary lattice, as opposed to the reciprocal one.

PROOF. Actually, it is sufficient to require that the scalar product of **K** with each of the primitive vectors $\mathbf{a}_1$, $\mathbf{a}_2$, $\mathbf{a}_3$ be an integral multiple of 2π. For let **K** be written in the form

$$\mathbf{K} = \lambda \mathbf{b}^1 + \mu \mathbf{b}^2 + \nu \mathbf{b}^3; \,' \qquad (2.19)$$

this can always[2] be done, though of course in general $\lambda\mu\nu$ need not be integers. Equation (2.15) then shows that the scalar products of **K** with the **a**'s are respectively $2\pi\lambda$, $2\pi\mu$, $2\pi\nu$, and since these are given to be integral multiples of 2π, the theorem is proved.

We conclude that in classifying the solutions of the dynamical problem by values of the vector **k**, it would be redundant to list two values of **k** which differ by a reciprocal lattice vector. In other words, **k** *should only run over a single primitive cell of the reciprocal lattice.*

2.5 Symmetry of Reciprocal Lattice; Examples

Since the reciprocal lattice is defined in terms of the primitive vectors of the direct lattice, which (as we saw in Sec. 1.4) are far from unique, it might be suspected that the reciprocal lattice itself is not unique. However, thanks to Theorems 2 and 3, we can define the reciprocal lattice equally well as *the set of vectors* **K** *whose scalar product with any direct lattice vector is an integral multiple of* 2π. This definition does not involve the primitive translation vectors, thus showing that a Bravais lattice has a unique reciprocal lattice associated with it. The further fact that *no two direct lattices can have the same reciprocal lattice* follows immediately from

Theorem 4. The reciprocal lattice of a reciprocal lattice is the original lattice.

The proof is in Problem 2 at the end of this chapter.

Suppose that we choose some point operation which leaves the direct lattice invariant and apply it to both the direct and the reciprocal lattice. Let this operation take **R** into **R'** and **K** into **K'**. The scalar product **K · R** is invariant under any point operation, so that **K' · R'** is an integral multiple of 2π; moreover, **R'** is a direct lattice vector by our choice of operation, and in fact can be made to be *any* direct lattice vector by choosing **R** correctly. Therefore, **K'** must be a reciprocal lattice vector, leading us to

Theorem 5. The direct and reciprocal lattices have all point operations in common; that is, they belong to the same crystal system.

---

[2] It is easily proved that the **b**'s are not coplanar; compare Problem 1 at the end of this chapter.

Some immediate conclusions can be drawn about those systems which contain only one Bravais lattice. Thus the reciprocal of a triclinic lattice is triclinic, the reciprocal of a rhombohedral lattice is rhombohedral, and the reciprocal of a hexagonal lattice is hexagonal. On the other hand, the monoclinic system has two lattices—simple and centered—and it is not *a priori* obvious whether each is its own reciprocal, or each is the reciprocal of the other.

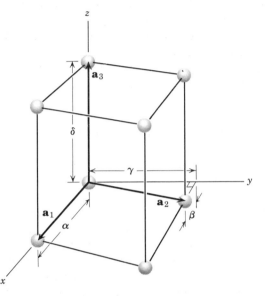

Fig. 2.1 Construction of a simple monoclinic primitive cell on Cartesian coordinates.

Let us examine this point. For the simple monoclinic lattice, we may take as primitive vectors in a Cartesian system

$$\mathbf{a}_1 = (\alpha, 0, 0); \quad \mathbf{a}_2 = (\beta, \gamma, 0); \quad \mathbf{a}_3 = (0, 0, \delta),$$

as indicated in Fig. 2.1. From the definitions (2.14) we then obtain

$$\mathbf{b}^1 = 2\pi\left(\frac{1}{\alpha}, \frac{-\beta}{\alpha\gamma}, 0\right); \qquad \mathbf{b}^2 = 2\pi\left(0, \frac{1}{\gamma}, 0\right);$$

$$\mathbf{b}^3 = 2\pi\left(0, 0, \frac{1}{\delta}\right).$$

These have the same form as the **a**'s, so that the reciprocal lattice is simple (Fig. 2.2). It follows that the reciprocal of the centered monoclinic is centered. It turns out that, of the fourteen Bravais lattices, there are only four which are not their own reciprocals; these are the body-centered and face-centered orthorhombic, and the body-centered and face-centered cubic. The proof is in Problem 3 at the end of this chapter.

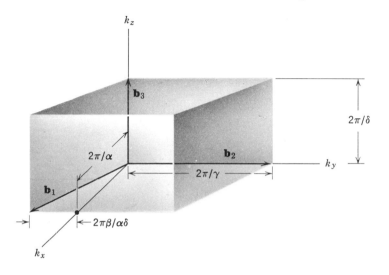

Fig. 2.2   The primitive cell which is reciprocal to Fig. 2.1 is also simple monoclinic.

2.6   Lattice Vectors and Lattice Planes

Theorem 6.   To every family of parallel planes of the direct lattice there corresponds a set of vectors of the reciprocal lattice which all point perpendicular to the planes. Moreover, the spacing of the planes is inversely proportional to the magnitude of the shortest vector of this set.

PROOF.   Reviewing the recipe for constructing primitive translation vectors of a lattice, we find that it is always possible to choose the first two, a_1 and a_2, to lie in any given lattice plane. The third one will then connect neighboring planes; that is, the component of a_3 perpendicular to the planes will be equal to the spacing between them.

If the set $a_1a_2a_3$ is now used to construct primitive reciprocal vectors by Eq. (2.14), it is clear that b^3, as well as all its multiples, will be perpendicular to the planes in question. The component of a_3 perpendicular to the planes can then be written

$$\frac{a_3 \cdot b^3}{|b^3|} = \frac{2\pi}{|b^3|} \; ; \tag{2.20}$$

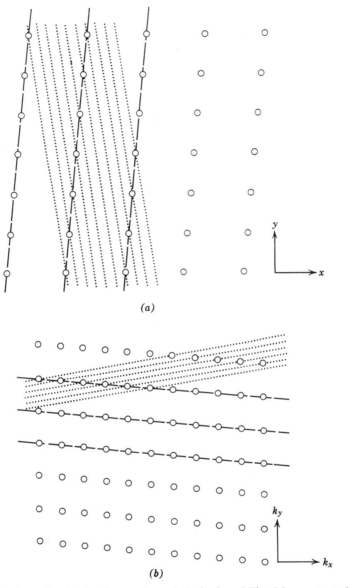

Fig. 2.3 Lines of points in the xy-plane of the lattice of Fig. 2.1 are perpendicular to planes of points in the reciprocal lattice. In (*a*), the dashed lines have a higher density of points than the dotted ones; in (*b*), the density of points in the corresponding dashed planes is proportionately higher than in the dotted ones.

and since $\mathbf{b}^3$ is the shortest reciprocal lattice vector in its direction, the proof of the theorem is completed.

It follows, incidentally, that the two-dimensional density of points in each of the planes, being equal to the three-dimensional lattice density multiplied by the spacing, is also inversely proportional to the shortest perpendicular reciprocal lattice vector. Figure 2.3 illustrates these relationships for the xy-plane of the monoclinic lattice of Figs. 2.1 and 2.2.

Theorem 7. To every reciprocal lattice vector $\mathbf{K}$ there corresponds a family of direct lattice planes perpendicular to it, whose spacing is inversely proportional to the shortest reciprocal lattice vector in the direction of $\mathbf{K}$.

PROOF. The trick here is not to define primitive vectors in the direct lattice, but to define primitive *reciprocal* vectors first. There is then sufficient freedom to choose $\mathbf{b}^1$ in the direction of $\mathbf{K}$; equal, in fact, to the shortest vector in that direction. The choice of $\mathbf{b}^2$ and $\mathbf{b}^3$ is then immaterial, for already the set $\mathbf{a}_1\mathbf{a}_2\mathbf{a}_3$ obtained from the $\mathbf{b}$'s by the inverse of Eq. (2.14) will have $\mathbf{a}_2$ and $\mathbf{a}_3$ perpendicular to $\mathbf{K}$. The existence of the family of planes in the direct lattice is thus proved, whereupon the numerical relations concerning their spacing follow from Theorem 6.

The preceding two theorems embody the essence of the relationship between a lattice and its reciprocal. To recapitulate: there is *no* correspondence of a particular point in a lattice to any point in the reciprocal lattice; there is *no* correspondence of a particular plane in a lattice to any point in the reciprocal lattice; there *is* a one-to-one correspondence between *possible directions* of planes in a lattice and *possible directions* of lines in its reciprocal lattice. This correspondence is quantitative in that planes of high density in one lattice are associated with lines of proportionately high density in the other.

2.7 Proximity Cell

We have previously used as a primitive cell the parallelepiped defined by the three primitive translation vectors. There are two disadvantages to this type of cell: it is not unique, and it does not, in general, possess the point symmetry of the lattice. One can construct a different type of cell by the following

Definition. The *proximity cell* associated with a particular lattice point consists of the region of space whose points are closer to that lattice point than they are to any other.

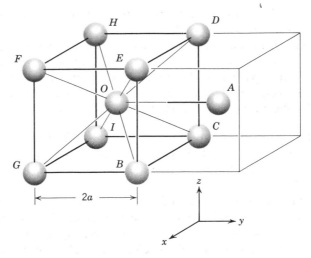

Fig. 2.4 First step in constructing the body-centered cubic proximity cell: the perpendicular bisectors of *OA* and equivalent segments produce a cube with lattice points at the corners.

Theorem 8. The proximity cells associated with all lattice points are identical in size, shape, and orientation. This follows from the translational symmetry of the lattice.

Theorem 9. When stacked, the proximity cells fill all of space.
PROOF. In order not to lie in *any* proximity cell, a point would have to be equally distant from at least two lattice points. But the loci of such points are planes, so that they do not occupy any finite volume.

Theorem 10. The proximity cell is a polyhedron.
PROOF. If we draw straight line segments connecting the central lattice

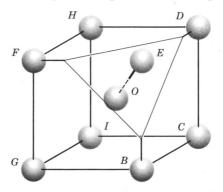

Fig. 2.5 Second step in constructing the body-centered cubic proximity cell: the perpendicular bisector of *OE* removes a corner of the cube.

point with every other, and construct the perpendicular bisector plane of each, the proximity cell will be that region of space which is on the near side of all these planes. Therefore, it is bounded by planes.

Theorem 11.   The proximity cell has the full point symmetry of its lattice point.

PROOF.   The proximity cell is unique; therefore, it is the same after any point operation.

As an example, let us construct the proximity cell for a body-centered cubic lattice. Put a lattice point at the origin; its near neighbors will then be six points with Cartesian coordinates which can be taken as $(\pm 2a, 0, 0)$, $(0, \pm 2a, 0)$, $(0, 0, \pm 2a)$; and eight body-center points at $(\pm a, \pm a, \pm a)$. Drawing the perpendicular bisector planes to the first six produces a cube having the body-center points at its corners, as in Fig. 2.4. Here O is the point at the origin, and A is at $(0, 2a, 0)$.

The next step is to draw the perpendicular bisector planes of OE, OB, etc. Figure 2.5 shows the remainder of the cube after the piece outside the perpendicular bisector of OE is discarded. After seven more slices (Fig. 2.6) we arrive at the desired proximity cell; for one easily convinces oneself that, although there are many more vectors still left in the lattice, all remaining perpendicular bisectors will fall outside the cell.

The phrase "proximity cell" is not generally used in the literature. If it is constructed in the direct lattice, it is called the *Wigner-Seitz unit cell*. If it is constructed in the reciprocal lattice, it is called the *(first) Brillouin zone*. The last paragraph of Sec. 2.4 can accordingly be restated as follows: *all possible solutions of the dynamical problem are obtained by considering only the values of* **k** *lying in the first Brillouin zone.*

2.8   Boundary Conditions

If the crystal were truly infinite in extent, there would be no boundary conditions on ξ other than its boundedness at infinity, which is assured by the fact that **k** is real. Actual crystals however, while usually very large compared to a lattice spacing, are not really infinite; this is sometimes important. For example, if the field in question has a finite number of degrees of freedom per cell, then the total crystal will also only have a finite number. This fact would be violated by the infinite number of normal modes obtained by letting **k** vary continuously. Clearly, it is necessary to invoke some boundary conditions at the positions where the crystal actually ends in order to resolve this situation.

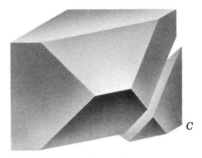

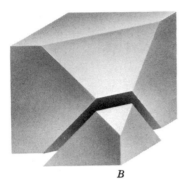

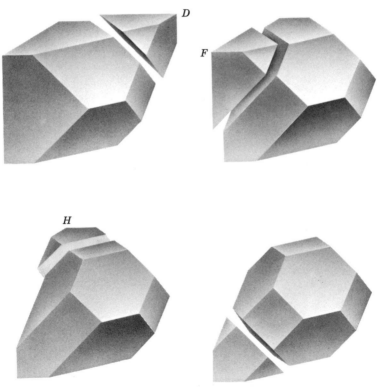

Fig. 2.6 Remaining steps in constructing the body-centered cubic proximity cell: removal of the other seven corners. The slices are labeled according to the atoms in Figs. 2.4 and 2.5; the final slice (*I*) is not visible in this view.

The difficulty is that as soon as we allow the lattice to end somewhere, the absolute position of a particular lattice point acquires physical significance, and the dynamical operator Ω ceases to commute with the translation operators. Thus, the formalism developed in previous sections becomes useless. In addition, the exact specification of boundary conditions is not only very complicated, but quite different for each specific field. On the other hand, we expect that bulk properties of the solid, that is, properties independent of surface structure, will not be changed if instead of using correct boundary conditions we substitute some mathematically more convenient ones.[3]

It turns out that it is possible to preserve the commutation of Ω with the translation operators at the cost of using boundary conditions which are physically absurd. These are called *periodic boundary conditions*. We shall first define them and examine some of their mathematical consequences; then return to the question of their justification in the next section.

Suppose we subdivide the (still infinite) crystal into large cells. These cells have boundaries parallel to those of a parallelepipedal primitive cell, but instead of edges $\mathbf{a}_1$, $\mathbf{a}_2$, $\mathbf{a}_3$ they have edges $L\mathbf{a}_1$, $M\mathbf{a}_2$, $N\mathbf{a}_3$. L, M, and N are very large integers, so that the large cell has the size of a macroscopic crystal. We then stipulate that the function ξ must be the same for corresponding small cells in each large cell (hence the name "periodic"). Thus, we limit the number of degrees of freedom to those in one large cell.

Since ξ has the form of Eq. (2.11), the requirement is that $e^{i\mathbf{k}\cdot\mathbf{R}}$ be periodic in the "large lattice" whose primitive translations are $L\mathbf{a}_1$, $M\mathbf{a}_2$, $N\mathbf{a}_3$, which is equivalent to restricting $\mathbf{k}$ to the vectors of the lattice reciprocal to the large one. Examination of Eq. (2.14) shows that the effect of scaling the $\mathbf{a}$'s up is to scale the $\mathbf{b}$'s down by the same factors; in other words, the allowed values of $\mathbf{k}$ form a lattice whose primitive vectors are $\mathbf{b}^1/L$, $\mathbf{b}^2/M$, and $\mathbf{b}^3/N$, so that we can write

$$\mathbf{k} = \frac{r_1}{L}\,\mathbf{b}^1 + \frac{r_2}{M}\,\mathbf{b}^2 + \frac{r_3}{N}\,\mathbf{b}^3 \qquad (2.21)$$

where the r's are integers.

As is shown in Problem 1, the product of the volumes of the primitive cells of two lattices which are each other's reciprocals is $(2\pi)^3$. It follows

---

[3] This is really a definition of "bulk properties"; what experience tells us is that bulk properties *exist*. Presumably that is due to the short-range nature of chemical forces; in systems such as plasmas, where long-range interactions are important, the distinction between "surface" and "bulk" cannot be as meaningful.

that the density of allowed **k**-values in the Brillouin zone is $V/(2\pi)^3$, where V is the volume of the "large cell" (which we shall identify with the whole crystal).

2.9 Physical Justification of Periodic Boundary Conditions

In order to justify the application of periodic boundary conditions, we must, of course, specify the use to which we are planning to put them. Now if we pick a particular **k** and substitute the form (2.11) into the dynamical problem (2.1) we obtain, in general, a discrete spectrum of eigenvalues which we may denote by $\lambda_j(\mathbf{k})$. As **k** is varied, each $\lambda_j(\mathbf{k})$ will vary, so that we may think of the eigenvalue as a many-valued function of **k**, with the index j numbering the various branches. Of course $\lambda_j(\mathbf{k})$ must be a periodic function of **k** with the periods of the reciprocal lattice, since in each primitive cell of the reciprocal lattice its values repeat.

The restriction to certain values of **k** imposed by periodic boundary conditions in turn limits $\lambda_j(\mathbf{k})$ to a discrete set, so that we may define a density of eigenvalues $\rho(\lambda)$ such that $\rho(\lambda)\, d\lambda$ is the number of allowed values of λ in the interval $d\lambda$.[4] To calculate $\rho(\lambda)\, d\lambda$ one would first identify the region of the Brillouin zone which corresponds to $\lambda_j(\mathbf{k})$ being in the interval between λ and $\lambda + d\lambda$, then multiply the volume of this region by $V/(2\pi)^3$, the density of allowed **k**-values in the zone, and finally sum over j. We shall now show that the function $\rho(\lambda)$ so calculated on the basis of periodic boundary conditions is in fact correct, except for some restrictions that will appear in the course of the discussion.

In doing this, it is convenient to use as an example a field with only a finite number of degrees of freedom, though the essential mathematical apparatus is (with some caution) applicable to other cases as well. Let us, therefore, investigate the vibrational modes of a crystal whose basis consists of single rigid atoms, one at each lattice point; let these atoms be connected by identical springs to their nearest neighbors. Imagine that each atom on a face of the crystal, whose shape is that of the "large cell" of the previous section, is connected by a similar spring and a massless rigid rod to its counterpart on the opposite face, as indicated in Fig. 2.7. Any normal mode of this system corresponds exactly to a normal mode of the infinite lattice on which periodic boundary conditions have been imposed; for in the latter case the atoms in the last layer would simply be coupled to the first layer of atoms in the next large cell, but since the

---

[4] We assume, of course, $d\lambda$ to be large enough to contain many eigenvalues, so that $\rho(\lambda)$ is a smooth function.

instantaneous displacement of those is the same as that of the first layer, the effect on the motion would be identical. Thus, in this case the periodic boundary conditions yield the correct normal modes.

Let us now ask what the effect would be on the distribution of normal frequencies if all the external springs in Fig. 2.7 were cut, thus reducing the system to the physically more palatable free boundary conditions.

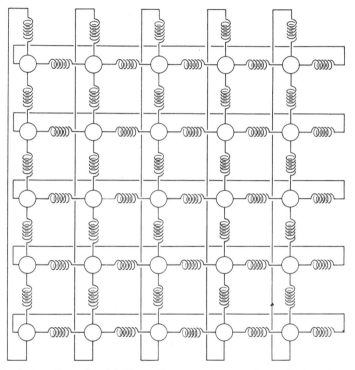

Fig. 2.7 A two-dimensional lattice with external connections which make periodic boundary conditions applicable.

We know from analytical dynamics that if we are given a mechanical system with N degrees of freedom (and therefore N normal modes), and we impose a constraint which reduces the number of degrees of freedom to $N - 1$, then the $N - 1$ new normal frequencies will be spaced between the N original frequencies. It follows that if a single spring constant of a system is changed, no characteristic frequency will shift further than the original position of either of its two neighboring frequencies. For let ω_n denote the frequencies of the original system and ω_n' those of the modified system, both numbered so that $n = 1$ denotes the lowest frequency, $n = 2$ the next lowest, and so on, $n = N$ being the highest one. Now if the particular spring in question is replaced by a rigid rod, this amounts to a constraint which reduces the number of degrees of freedom to $N - 1$; let the characteristic frequencies of this constrained system, again numbered in ascending order, be $\Omega_1, \Omega_2, \ldots \Omega_{N-1}$. We then have

$$\omega_1 < \Omega_1 < \omega_2 \qquad\qquad \omega_1' < \Omega_1 < \omega_2'$$

$$\omega_2 < \Omega_2 < \omega_3 \qquad\qquad \omega_2' < \Omega_2 < \omega_3'$$

$$\cdot$$
$$\cdot \qquad\qquad\qquad\qquad\qquad (2.22)$$
$$\cdot$$

$$\omega_{N-1} < \Omega_{N-1} < \omega_N \qquad \omega_{N-1}' < \Omega_{N-1} < \omega_N'.$$

Combining these inequalities, we find

$$\omega_1' < \omega_2$$

$$\omega_1 < \omega_2' < \omega_3$$

$$\omega_2 < \omega_3' < \omega_4$$

$$\cdot$$
$$\cdot \qquad\qquad\qquad\qquad\qquad (2.23)$$
$$\cdot$$

$$\omega_{N-1} < \omega_N'.$$

With this result we are in a position to answer the question as to what happens if the external springs in Fig. 2.7 are cut: No characteristic frequency will shift further than the original position of its νth neighbor, ν being the number of springs to be removed. Assuming that *the number of atoms on the surface of the crystal is negligible compared to the total number*, one sees that the shift will be a negligible fraction of the total spectrum. In fact, we can state that $\rho(\lambda)\, d\lambda$ will be correctly given by periodic boundary conditions *provided that $d\lambda$ contains a number of eigenvalues large compared to the number of surface atoms*.

It is clear that the imposition of any boundary conditions other than the "free" ones still allows the same type of argument to proceed; the only question remaining to be examined is that of the crystal not being parallelepipedal in shape. But, since there is a good deal of freedom in choosing the shape of the parallelepiped, we can generally consider an arbitrarily shaped body as being constructed from a *relatively* small number of coupled parallelepipeds, with a *relatively* small number of surface atoms rearranged. Note, however, that the validity of periodic boundary conditions does require some physical criteria to be satisfied. If the material is in the form of a very fine powder, or of a single crystal of extremely convoluted shape, it may well exhibit properties which such boundary conditions fail to predict. As compared to "bulk properties," these "surface properties" are generally much more complex in their description, since they specifically depend on the surface structure of the specimen.

2.10   Properties of Allowed Lattice Exponentials

Theorem 12.   If k and k′ are two k-vectors allowed by the periodic boundary conditions, then

$$\sum_{\mathbf{R}} e^{-i\mathbf{k}' \cdot \mathbf{R}} e^{i\mathbf{k} \cdot \mathbf{R}} = \mathcal{N} \delta_{\mathbf{kk}'}, \tag{2.24}$$

where the summation is over all the lattice points of a large cell, $\delta_{\mathbf{kk}'}$ is the Kronecker symbol, and $\mathcal{N}$ is the number of lattice points.
PROOF.   According to Eq. (2.21),

$$\mathbf{k} = \frac{r_1}{L} \mathbf{b}^1 + \frac{r_2}{M} \mathbf{b}^2 + \frac{r_3}{N} \mathbf{b}^3$$

$$\mathbf{k}' = \frac{r_1'}{L} \mathbf{b}^1 + \frac{r_2'}{M} \mathbf{b}^2 + \frac{r_3'}{N} \mathbf{b}^3;$$

also, from Eq. (1.1),

$$\mathbf{R} = l\mathbf{a}_1 + m\mathbf{a}_2 + n\mathbf{a}_3.$$

Therefore

$$\sum_{\mathbf{R}} e^{-i\mathbf{k}' \cdot \mathbf{R}} e^{i\mathbf{k} \cdot \mathbf{R}} = \sum_{l=0}^{L-1} \sum_{m=0}^{M-1} \sum_{n=0}^{N-1}$$

$$\times \exp \left\{ 2\pi i \left[\frac{l(r_1 - r_1')}{L} + \frac{m(r_2 - r_2')}{M} + \frac{n(r_3 - r_3')}{N} \right] \right\}$$

$$= \frac{1 - e^{2\pi i (r_1 - r_1')}}{1 - e^{2\pi i (r_1 - r_1')/L}} \frac{1 - e^{2\pi i (r_2 - r_2')}}{1 - e^{2\pi i (r_2 - r_2')/M}}$$

$$\times \frac{1 - e^{2\pi i (r_3 - r_3')}}{1 - e^{2\pi i (r_3 - r_3')/N}}. \tag{2.25}$$

Let us examine the first of these three factors. Since k and k′ are both in the same primitive cell of the reciprocal lattice, we must have $r_1 - r_1' < L$. Therefore, the denominator cannot vanish unless $r_1 = r_1'$.

But since r_1 and r_1' are integers, the numerator always vanishes. Therefore, the right-hand side of Eq. (2.25) is zero unless the three conditions $r_1 = r_1'$, $r_2 = r_2'$, $r_3 = r_3'$ are all satisfied, which would mean $\mathbf{k}' = \mathbf{k}$. But if the two $\mathbf{k}$'s are equal, every term in Eq. (2.24) is unity, so that the sum is simply equal to the number of terms.

Theorem 13. If $\mathbf{R}$ and $\mathbf{R}'$ are two lattice vectors, then

$$\sum_{BZ} e^{-i\mathbf{k}\cdot\mathbf{R}'} e^{i\mathbf{k}\cdot\mathbf{R}} = \mathcal{N}\delta_{\mathbf{R}\mathbf{R}'} \qquad (2.26)$$

where the sum is over all allowed values of $\mathbf{k}$ in the Brillouin zone.
PROOF. Since Eq. (2.26) will not be changed if we change some $\mathbf{k}$'s by adding reciprocal lattice vectors, we can equally well perform the summations over a parallelepipedal primitive cell of the reciprocal lattice. That is, we make the replacement

$$\sum_{BZ} \rightarrow \sum_{r_1=0}^{L-1} \sum_{r_2=0}^{M-1} \sum_{r_3=0}^{N-1}$$

the r's being those of Eq. (2.21). The proof then follows in analogy with the preceding theorem.

Corollary 1. The exponentials $e^{i\mathbf{k}\cdot\mathbf{R}}$ constitute a complete set for the expansion of any lattice function; that is, given a set of numbers $F(\mathbf{R})$, one for each lattice point, we can find a set of numbers $A_\mathbf{k}$ such that

$$F(\mathbf{R}) = \sum_{BZ} A_\mathbf{k} e^{i\mathbf{k}\cdot\mathbf{R}}. \qquad (2.27)$$

PROOF. Let

$$A_\mathbf{k} = \frac{1}{\mathcal{N}} \sum_{\mathbf{R}'} e^{-i\mathbf{k}\cdot\mathbf{R}'} F(\mathbf{R}'). \qquad (2.28)$$

Then

$$\sum_{BZ} A_\mathbf{k} e^{i\mathbf{k}\cdot\mathbf{R}} = \frac{1}{\mathcal{N}} \sum_{BZ} \sum_{\mathbf{R}'} e^{-i\mathbf{k}\cdot\mathbf{R}'} e^{i\mathbf{k}\cdot\mathbf{R}} F(\mathbf{R}')$$

$$= \sum_{\mathbf{R}'} F(\mathbf{R}')\delta_{\mathbf{R}\mathbf{R}'} = F(\mathbf{R}).$$

Corollary 2. For a given $F(\mathbf{R})$, the set $A_\mathbf{k}$ is unique. The proof is in Problem 4.

With these theorems we have completed the general mathematical background for discussing waves in lattices, and can proceed to the solution of more specific problems.

PROBLEMS

1. Prove that the product of the primitive cell volumes in the direct and reciprocal lattices is $(2\pi)^3$.

2. Prove that the reciprocal lattice of a reciprocal lattice is the original lattice.

3. (*a*) Prove that the body-centered and face-centered orthorhombic lattices are each others' reciprocals.

   (*b*) Would you consider the same fact about the face-centered and body-centered cubic lattices a simple corollary of (*a*), or does it require separate proof?

4. Prove Corollary 2 on page 48.

3

Vibration Spectrum of a Lattice

3.1 Introduction

If the atoms comprising a crystal were rigid masses connected by massless springs, as we took them to be for illustrative purposes in the discussion of the last chapter, there would be no difficulty in defining a type of motion to which the name "lattice vibration" could be applied. In fact, however, the atoms consist of nuclei surrounded by electrons, so that they can hardly be described as rigid, in addition to which the "massless springs" do not exist.

The type of argument which nevertheless allows us to define such a type of motion is called the *adiabatic approximation*. In the following sections we shall develop the basic ideas of the method by discussing an idealized example in some detail, namely, the motion of two coupled degrees of freedom the ratio of whose characteristic masses is very large. It will be seen that the type of reasoning used can be extended to problems of many more degrees of freedom, provided the classification into high-mass and low-mass motions can be made.

3.2 Adiabatic Basis

We begin with a Hamiltonian

$$H = \frac{P^2}{2M} + \frac{p^2}{2m} + W(q - Q) \tag{3.1}$$

where P and p are the momenta conjugate to Q and q respectively, and it is assumed that $M \gg m$. A complete orthonormal set of functions $\Psi_{n\lambda}(q, Q)$ is now constructed by the following recipe:

1. The equation

$$\left[\frac{p^2}{2m} + W(q - Q)\right]\varphi_{nQ}(q) = \epsilon_n(Q)\varphi_{nQ}(q) \tag{3.2}$$

is solved for the eigenvalues $\epsilon_n(Q)$ and the eigenfunctions $\varphi_{nQ}(q)$ with Q regarded as a fixed parameter. This solution is carried out for each value of Q. The φ_{nQ}'s are normalized and have their phases adjusted so that they are all real (which can always be done for a real Hamiltonian).

The ordinary eigenvalue theory then tells us that, for each Q, the φ's form a complete orthonormal[1] set:

$$\int \varphi_{n'Q}(q)\varphi_{nQ}(q)\, dq = \delta_{n'n}; \tag{3.3}$$

$$\sum_n \varphi_{nQ}(q')\varphi_{nQ}(q) = \delta(q' - q). \tag{3.4}$$

2. The equation

$$\left[\frac{P^2}{2M} + \epsilon_n(Q)\right]\chi_{n\lambda}(Q) = E_{n\lambda}\chi_{n\lambda}(Q) \tag{3.5}$$

is then solved for the eigenvalues $E_{n\lambda}$ and the eigenfunctions $\chi_{n\lambda}(Q)$. This process has to be carried out separately for each n. The eigenfunctions satisfy

$$\int \chi^*_{n\lambda'}(Q)\chi_{n\lambda}(Q)\, dQ = \delta_{\lambda'\lambda} \tag{3.6}$$

$$\sum_\lambda \chi^*_{n\lambda}(Q')\chi_{n\lambda}(Q) = \delta(Q' - Q). \tag{3.7}$$

(The phases of the χ's are immaterial.)

3. The desired functions $\Psi_{n\lambda}(q, Q)$ are now defined by

$$\Psi_{n\lambda}(q, Q) \equiv \chi_{n\lambda}(Q)\varphi_{nQ}(q). \tag{3.8}$$

It follows that

$$\int \Psi^*_{n'\lambda'}(q, Q)\Psi_{n\lambda}(q, Q)\, dq\, dQ = \int \chi^*_{n'\lambda'}(Q)\chi_{n\lambda}(Q)\, \delta_{n'n}\, dQ$$

$$= \delta_{n'n} \int \chi^*_{n\lambda'}(Q)\chi_{n\lambda}(Q)\, dQ$$

$$= \delta_{n'n}\, \delta_{\lambda'\lambda}; \tag{3.9}$$

---

[1] We assume the reader to be familiar with the procedure by which degenerate φ's, which are not automatically orthogonal, can nevertheless be made so.

also,

$$\sum_{n\lambda} \Psi_{n\lambda}^*(q', Q')\Psi_{n\lambda}(q, Q) = \sum_{n} \varphi_{nQ'}^*(q')\varphi_{nQ}(q)\,\delta(Q' - Q)$$

$$= \delta(Q' - Q) \sum_{n} \varphi_{nQ}^*(q')\varphi_{nQ}(q)$$

$$= \delta(Q' - Q)\,\delta(q' - q). \qquad (3.10)$$

Thus, the Ψ's do form a complete orthonormal set, as previously asserted, and provide a valid basis for an *exact* quantum-mechanical representation.

3.3   Matrix Elements of Hamiltonian

The adiabatic *approximation* consists in asserting that the $\Psi_{n\lambda}$'s are eigenfunctions of the Hamiltonian, with the $E_{n\lambda}$'s the respective eigenvalues. To examine the validity of such an assertion, let us apply the Hamiltonian to one of the Ψ's. The result is

$$H\Psi_{n\lambda} = \left[\frac{P^2}{2M} + \frac{p^2}{2m} + W(q - Q)\right]\chi_{n\lambda}(Q)\varphi_{nQ}(q)$$

$$= \frac{P^2}{2M}\chi_{n\lambda}(Q)\varphi_{nQ}(q) + \chi_{n\lambda}(Q)\left[\frac{p^2}{2m} + W(q - Q)\right]\varphi_{nQ}(q)$$

$$= \left[\frac{P^2}{2M} + \epsilon_n(Q)\right]\chi_{n\lambda}(Q)\varphi_{nQ}(q)$$

$$= E_{n\lambda}\Psi_{n\lambda} + \frac{1}{2M}\{2[P\chi_{n\lambda}(Q)][P\varphi_{nQ}(q)] + \chi_{n\lambda}(Q)P^2\varphi_{nQ}(q)\}, \quad (3.11)$$

where in the last line the role of P as a differential operator has been used. It is now apparent that the first term corresponds to the adiabatic approximation. To see how large the other terms are, let us first investigate the matrix element $\langle n\lambda'|H|n\lambda\rangle$ in which the two n's are the same. The contribution of the first term in the braces is

$$\frac{\hbar}{iM}\int dQ\chi_{n\lambda'}^*(Q)P\chi_{n\lambda}(Q)\int dq\,\varphi_{nQ}(q)\frac{\partial}{\partial Q}\varphi_{nQ}(q), \qquad (3.12)$$

which is zero, as is easily shown by differentiating the normalization condition (3.3) (the importance of choosing the φ's real shows itself here). The remaining term is

$$-\frac{\hbar^2}{2M}\int dQ\chi_{n\lambda'}^*(Q)\chi_{n\lambda}(Q)\int dq\,\varphi_{nQ}(q)\frac{\partial^2}{\partial Q^2}\varphi_{nQ}(q), \qquad (3.13)$$

which we handle by the following argument. It is clear from the form of Eq. (3.2) that $\varphi_{nQ}(q)$ is actually a function of the difference $q - Q$, so that $\partial^2\varphi_{nQ}/\partial Q^2 = \partial^2\varphi_{nQ}/\partial q^2$; but we do not want to use this fact, since it is only true in the special model containing only one q and one Q. However, an *approximate* equality of the same sort must hold in general because of the nature of W as an interaction energy, whose sensitivity to changes in q and Q must be of comparable order of magnitude. Therefore, we make the *approximate* substitution $\partial^2/\partial Q^2 \to \partial^2/\partial q^2$, obtaining

$$\langle n\lambda' \,|H|\, n\lambda \rangle \cong \frac{m}{M} \int dQ \chi^*_{n\lambda'}(Q)\chi_{n\lambda}(Q) \int dq\, \varphi_{nQ}(q) \frac{p^2}{2m}\, \varphi_{nQ}(q). \quad (3.14)$$

The last integral is the expectation value of the kinetic energy in state φ_{nQ}, which must be of the same order of magnitude as the eigenvalue $\epsilon_n(Q)$. Thus

$$\langle n\lambda' \,|H|\, n\lambda \rangle \cong \frac{m}{M} \int \chi^*_{n\lambda'}(Q)\epsilon_n(Q)\chi_{n\lambda}(Q)\, dQ. \quad (3.15)$$

Finally, we define a quantity Δ as the typical energy magnitude in the "heavy" spectrum, that is, the spectrum of Eq. (3.5) for a particular n; then the last integral, being a matrix element of the effective potential energy, will be of order Δ (or perhaps much less if λ and λ' are very different). Therefore, an upper limit on the matrix element is given by

$$\langle n\lambda' \,|H|\, n\lambda \rangle \lesssim \frac{m}{M}\, \Delta. \quad (3.16)$$

In general, the fractional effect of a perturbation in the Hamiltonian is given by the ratio of a typical matrix element of the perturbation to a typical energy difference in the unperturbed spectrum. Since the latter is, in our case, approximately equal to Δ, we see that the fractional effect of matrix elements diagonal in n is of order m/M.

As for the matrix elements with $n' \neq n$, Eq. (3.11) gives

$$\langle n'\lambda' \,|H|\, n\lambda \rangle = \frac{1}{M} \int dQ \chi^*_{n'\lambda'}(Q) P \chi_{n\lambda}(Q) \int dq\, \varphi_{n'Q}(q) P \varphi_{nQ}(q)$$

$$+ \frac{1}{2M} \int dQ \chi^*_{n'\lambda'}(Q)\chi_{n\lambda}(Q) \int dq\, \varphi_{n'Q}(q) P^2 \varphi_{nQ}(q). \quad (3.17)$$

It is easy to show that the last term has the same order of magnitude as it had for $n' = n$; however, the first term no longer vanishes. To estimate its magnitude, we again make the replacement $P \to p$ in the q-integral, which then becomes the matrix element of momentum between two solutions of Eq. (3.2). Thus, the whole first term will be of order of magnitude

$$\frac{1}{M}(M\Delta)^{\frac{1}{2}}(m\delta)^{\frac{1}{2}} = \left(\frac{\Delta\delta m}{M}\right)^{\frac{1}{2}}$$

where δ is a typical energy magnitude in the "light" spectrum. This matrix element is larger than the one of Eq. (3.16) by the factor $(M \delta/m \Delta)^{\frac{1}{2}}$, which by our assumptions is large. It is, however, to be compared to δ, the energy interval between the states which it connects; the relevant fractional perturbation is then $(m \Delta/M \delta)^{\frac{1}{2}}$, a small number. Thus for $m \ll M$ and $\Delta \ll \delta$ the adiabatic approximation has been justified.

3.4 Vibration Hamiltonian

By the problem of "vibration of a crystal" we mean the motion which is governed by a Hamiltonian corresponding to Eq. (3.1), with many Q's representing displacements of nuclei, and q's representing electrons; $\epsilon_n(Q)$ is then the energy eigenvalue of the electronic motion with the nuclei considered fixed. We shall denote by V the total potential energy of nuclear motion, which includes, in addition to $\epsilon_n(Q)$, the electrostatic repulsion between nuclei. Without loss of generality, V may be taken to be zero for the equilibrium configuration. For small nuclear displacements, it must then be a quadratic function of these displacements, since the derivative of the energy with respect to each nuclear displacement must vanish.

Let $x_i(n; \alpha)$ be the i-component ($i = 1, 2, 3$) of displacement of the αth atom in the primitive cell labeled by the lattice vector $\mathbf{R}_n$; a particular α refers to corresponding atoms in different cells. Then the potential energy for small displacements is

$$V = \frac{1}{2} \sum_{nmij\alpha\beta} \varkappa_{\alpha i;\,\beta j}(\mathbf{R}_n - \mathbf{R}_m)x_i(n; \alpha)x_j(m; \beta). \tag{3.18}$$

Because of the mathematical form of Eq. (3.18), we are free to impose the condition

$$\varkappa_{\alpha i;\,\beta j}(\mathbf{R}_n - \mathbf{R}_m) = \varkappa_{\beta j;\,\alpha i}(\mathbf{R}_m - \mathbf{R}_n). \tag{3.19}$$

Differentiating (3.18) with respect to a particular x, say $x_k(l; \gamma)$, we obtain

$$\frac{\partial V}{\partial x_k(l; \gamma)} = \sum_{ni\alpha} \varkappa_{\alpha i;\,\gamma k}(\mathbf{R}_n - \mathbf{R}_l)x_i(n; \alpha), \tag{3.20}$$

by using (3.19) and the dummy index rule. Now let one of the x's, say $x_j(m; \beta)$, be equal to unity, and let all the others be zero. Equation (3.20) then becomes

$$\frac{\partial V}{\partial x_k(l; \gamma)} = \varkappa_{\beta j; \gamma k}(\mathbf{R}_m - \mathbf{R}_l). \tag{3.21}$$

This shows that $\varkappa_{\beta j; \gamma k}(\mathbf{R}_m - \mathbf{R}_l)$ has the significance of being *the negative of the k-component of force exerted on atom* $(l; \gamma)$ *due to unit displacement in the j-direction of atom* $(m; \beta)$. Because of Eq. (3.19), it is at the same time *the negative of the j-component of force exerted on atom* $(m; \beta)$ *due to unit displacement in the k-direction of atom* $(l; \gamma)$. From this and the equivalence of cells of the crystal, it follows that the $\varkappa$'s can only depend on the difference $\mathbf{R}_m - \mathbf{R}_l$, a fact already incorporated into our notation. Note also that if every atom in the crystal is given an equal displacement in the i-direction, no force on any atom will result, so that

$$\sum_{n\alpha} \varkappa_{\alpha i; \beta j}(\mathbf{R}_n - \mathbf{R}_m) = 0 \tag{3.22}$$

for any choice of i, j, β, and m. This condition embodies the invariance of the crystal *as a whole* to infinitesimal translations.

Another condition on the "force constants" arises from the fact that the lattice can be in equilibrium under a uniform strain.[2] Such a strain is described by the *center* of each cell being displaced by an amount proportional to its position; in addition, some internal distortion of each cell is to be expected, giving rise to piezoelectricity and similar phenomena. The general atomic displacement then takes the form

$$x_i(n; \alpha) = \mathbf{\Phi}^{(i)} \cdot \mathbf{R}_n + \varphi_i(\alpha); \tag{3.23}$$

the $\mathbf{\Phi}^{(i)}$ are three arbitrary constant vectors, and the φ's (which describe the internal strain) depend on the $\mathbf{\Phi}$'s. The mathematical statement of equilibrium under a uniform strain is then the following: for any three vectors $\mathbf{\Phi}^{(i)}$, there exist $3\mathscr{R}$ numbers $\varphi_i(\alpha)$ such that the atomic displacement (3.23) gives rise to zero force on each atom; or

$$\sum_{in\alpha} \varkappa_{\alpha i; \beta j}(\mathbf{R}_n)[\mathbf{\Phi}^{(i)} \cdot \mathbf{R}_n + \varphi_i(\alpha)] = 0. \tag{3.24}$$

The unknown φ's can be eliminated by summing Eq. (3.23) over β, for then the second term becomes

$$\sum_{in\alpha\beta} \varkappa_{\alpha i; \beta j}(\mathbf{R}_n)\varphi_i(\alpha) = \sum_{i\alpha} \varphi_i(\alpha) \sum_{n\beta} \varkappa_{\alpha i; \beta j}(\mathbf{R}_n) = 0 \tag{3.25}$$

---

[2] In an actual crystal, the maintenance of a uniform strain requires external forces on the *surface atoms*. Our model of an infinite crystal does not contain any surface atoms, i.e., we are studying the interior atoms only.

by Eq. (3.22). Therefore

$$\sum_{i n \alpha \beta} \varkappa_{\alpha i; \beta j}(\mathbf{R}_n)\mathbf{\Phi}^{(i)} \cdot \mathbf{R}_n = 0; \tag{3.26}$$

and since the $\mathbf{\Phi}$'s are arbitrary,

$$\sum_{n \alpha \beta} \varkappa_{\alpha i; \beta j}(\mathbf{R}_n)\mathbf{R}_n = 0. \tag{3.27}$$

Equation (3.27) is the required restriction on the $\varkappa$'s.[3]

Finally, the total Hamiltonian for vibrations of the crystal is

$$H = \frac{1}{2}\sum_{n \alpha i} \frac{[p_i(n; \alpha)]^2}{M_\alpha} + \frac{1}{2}\sum_{\substack{n \alpha i \\ m \beta j}} \varkappa_{\alpha i; \beta j}(\mathbf{R}_n - \mathbf{R}_m)x_i(n; \alpha)x_j(m; \beta) \tag{3.28}$$

where $p_i(n; \alpha)$ is the momentum corresponding to the displacement $x_i(n; \alpha)$, and M_α the mass of the αth atom in the primitive cell.

3.5 Classical Normal Modes

Even though the potential, of which the $\varkappa$'s are the second derivatives, is of quantum-mechanical origin, it is interesting to investigate the motion of the nuclei considered as classical particles. Applying to (3.28) the equations of motion

$$\dot{x}_k(l; \gamma) = \frac{\partial H}{\partial p_k(l; \gamma)} ; \qquad \dot{p}_k(l; \gamma) = -\frac{\partial H}{\partial x_k(l; \gamma)} \tag{3.29}$$

and eliminating the momenta, we find (with an additional change in indices)

$$-M_\alpha \ddot{x}_i(n; \alpha) = \sum_{m \beta j} \varkappa_{\alpha i; \beta j}(\mathbf{R}_n - \mathbf{R}_m)x_j(m; \beta). \tag{3.30}$$

The *normal modes* are those motions which vary sinusoidally in time with some frequency ω, so that for them the second time-derivative can be replaced by $-\omega^2$. The equation then takes the form (2.1); hence, solutions

---

[3] It is possible to imagine systems which violate Eq. 3.27. For example, a lattice of negative point charges can be in equilibrium in a uniform fixed background density of positive charges. However, a uniform dilation of the point charge spacing would produce a net space charge, and hence, a restoring force on *every* "atom." It is well known that a charged plasma of this type does not have any "sound waves" in the sense of low-frequency excitations whose frequency is proportional to the propagation vector, and, indeed, we shall see in Sec. 3.6 that in order to prove the existence of sound waves in a solid Eq. 3.27 must be assumed.

of the type

$$x_i(n; \alpha) = \xi_i(\mathbf{k}; \alpha)e^{i\mathbf{k} \cdot \mathbf{R}_n} \tag{3.31}$$

must exist. Substitution into Eq. (3.30) yields

$$M_\alpha \omega^2 \xi_i(\mathbf{k}; \alpha)e^{i\mathbf{k} \cdot \mathbf{R}_n} = \sum_{m\beta j} \varkappa_{\alpha i; \beta j}(\mathbf{R}_n - \mathbf{R}_m)\xi_j(\mathbf{k}; \beta)e^{i\mathbf{k} \cdot \mathbf{R}_m}; \tag{3.32}$$

or

$$\sum_{\beta j} \Gamma_{\alpha i; \beta j}(\mathbf{k})\xi_j(\mathbf{k}; \beta) = M_\alpha \omega^2 \xi_i(\mathbf{k}; \alpha), \tag{3.33}$$

where

$$\Gamma_{\alpha i; \beta j}(\mathbf{k}) \equiv \sum_{\mathbf{R}} \varkappa_{\alpha i; \beta j}(\mathbf{R})e^{-i\mathbf{k} \cdot \mathbf{R}}. \tag{3.34}$$

Making the further substitutions

$$\eta_i(\mathbf{k}; \alpha) \equiv M_\alpha^{1/2} \xi_i(\mathbf{k}; \alpha) \tag{3.35}$$

$$\Omega_{\alpha i; \beta j}(\mathbf{k}) \equiv \frac{\Gamma_{\alpha i; \beta j}(\mathbf{k})}{(M_\alpha M_\beta)^{1/2}}, \tag{3.36}$$

we get

$$\sum_{\beta j} \Omega_{\alpha i; \beta j}(\mathbf{k})\eta_j(\mathbf{k}; \beta) = \omega^2 \eta_i(\mathbf{k}; \alpha). \tag{3.37}$$

Since α and β run from 1 to $\mathscr{R}$, where $\mathscr{R}$ is the number of atoms in a primitive cell, and i and j from 1 to 3, Eq. (3.37) is actually an eigenvalue problem for the $3\mathscr{R} \times 3\mathscr{R}$ matrix $\Omega(\mathbf{k})$. By diagonalizing it we obtain three frequencies for each value of $\mathbf{k}$, which we denote by $\omega_\lambda(\mathbf{k})$ ($\lambda = 1, 2, 3$), corresponding to eigenvectors $\eta_i{}^\lambda(\mathbf{k}; \alpha)$. The eigenvectors can be made to satisfy the usual orthonormality and completeness relations

$$\sum_{i\alpha} \eta_i{}^\lambda(\mathbf{k}; \alpha)^* \eta_i{}^\mu(\mathbf{k}; \alpha) = \delta_{\lambda\mu} \tag{3.38}$$

$$\sum_{\lambda} \eta_i{}^\lambda(\mathbf{k}; \alpha)^* \eta_j{}^\lambda(\mathbf{k}; \beta) = \delta_{ij} \delta_{\alpha\beta}. \tag{3.39}$$

There are precisely $\mathscr{N}$ allowed values of $\mathbf{k}$ in the Brillouin zone, so the method yields $3\mathscr{R}\mathscr{N}$ normal modes—exactly equal to the number of degrees of freedom of the crystal. Note how the use of translational invariance of the crystal, embodied in the form (3.31), reduces the original $3\mathscr{R}\mathscr{N}$-dimensional dynamical matrix to $\mathscr{N}$ matrices of dimensionality $3\mathscr{R}$ each.

From Eqs. (3.34) and (3.36) we see that

$$\Omega_{\alpha i; \beta j}(-\mathbf{k}) = \Omega_{\alpha i; \beta j}(\mathbf{k})^*. \tag{3.40}$$

Therefore, the complex conjugate of $\eta_i{}^\lambda(\mathbf{k}; \alpha)$ must be an eigenvector of $\Omega(-\mathbf{k})$ with eigenvalue $\omega_\lambda(\mathbf{k})^{2*}$. But since Ω is Hermitian, its eigenvalues must be real,[4] so that we can write

$$\omega_\lambda(\mathbf{k}) = \omega_\lambda(-\mathbf{k}) \tag{3.41}$$

in addition to $\qquad\qquad \eta_i^\lambda(-\mathbf{k};\alpha) = \eta_i^\lambda(\mathbf{k};\alpha)^*. \tag{3.42}$

The latter condition is not, incidentally, automatically satisfied, for an arbitrary phase factor can be attached to $\eta(\mathbf{k})$ and/or to $\eta(-\mathbf{k})$. Rather, it represents a restriction which we can impose, by virtue of which the phases of $\eta(\mathbf{k})$ and $\eta(-\mathbf{k})$ become dependent on each other.

3.6 Acoustical and Optical Branches

From Eqs. (3.34) and (3.22) it follows that

$$\sum_\beta \Gamma_{\alpha i;\,\beta j}(0) = 0, \tag{3.43}$$

so that [by direct substitution into Eq. (3.33)] solutions of the dynamical problem with $\mathbf{k} = 0$ and $\omega = 0$ can be constructed by making $\xi_j(0;\beta)$ independent of β. Since j can take on three values, there are three linearly independent vectors of this form. Thus, of the $3\mathscr{R}$ "branches" of the vibrational spectrum there are always three which go to zero frequency at $\mathbf{k} = 0$.[5]

The behavior of these branches for $\mathbf{k}$ *near* zero can be obtained by perturbation theory. Let the three (unnormalized) eigenvectors with $\omega = 0$ at $\mathbf{k} = 0$ be

$$\xi_i^\lambda(0;\alpha) = \delta_{i\lambda} \tag{3.44}$$

with $\lambda = 1, 2$, and 3. From these we construct the eigenvectors of Ω with the aid of Eqs. (3.35) and (3.38):

$$\eta_i^\lambda(0;\alpha) = \left(\frac{M_\alpha}{M}\right)^{\!1/2} \delta_{i\lambda} \tag{3.45}$$

where $\qquad\qquad\qquad M = \sum_\alpha M_\alpha. \tag{3.46}$

---

[4] Actually, the eigenvalues ω^2 must be *real and positive* in order to have the frequencies real. An imaginary ω would mean a normal mode which varies exponentially rather than sinusoidally in time. The condition that all eigenvalues of Ω must be positive is, indirectly, a restriction on the force constants; it is clear physically that this condition is equivalent to the requirement that V be positive definite, i.e., that the equilibrium configuration $x = 0$ be stable.

[5] Obviously, these solutions with $\mathbf{k} = 0$ and ξ independent of β describe a rigid translation of the crystal as a whole. That such a motion is a normal mode with zero frequency is due to our stipulation in Eq. (3.22) that no restoring force on any atom results from it.

We must next construct the submatrix of $\Omega(\mathbf{k})$ corresponding to the three degenerate eigenvectors (3.45):

$$\langle \eta^\lambda \, |\Omega(\mathbf{k})| \, \eta^\mu \rangle \equiv \sum_{ij\alpha\beta} \eta_i^\lambda(0;\alpha)^* \Omega_{\alpha i;\,\beta j}(\mathbf{k}) \eta_j^\mu(0;\beta)$$

$$= M^{-1} \sum_{\alpha\beta n} \varkappa_{\alpha\lambda;\,\beta\mu}(\mathbf{R}_n) e^{-i\mathbf{k}\cdot\mathbf{R}_n}. \tag{3.46}$$

For small values of $\mathbf{k}$ (which we must assume for perturbation theory to be applicable) the exponential in Eq. (3.46) can be expanded in a power series[6] with the result

$$\langle \eta^\lambda \, |\Omega(\mathbf{k})| \, \eta^\mu \rangle \cong \mathbf{k} \cdot \mathbf{F}(\lambda\mu) \cdot \mathbf{k}, \tag{3.47}$$

where the dyadic $\mathbf{F}(\lambda\mu)$ is given by

$$\mathbf{F}(\lambda\mu) \equiv -\frac{1}{2} \sum_{\alpha\beta n} \mathbf{R}_n \mathbf{R}_n \varkappa_{\alpha\lambda;\,\beta\mu}(\mathbf{R}_n). \tag{3.48}$$

The reader may convince himself that due to Eqs. (3.22) and (3.27) both the constant term and the linear term in the expansion of (3.46) vanish.

Equation (3.47) shows that, for small $\mathbf{k}$, the matrix elements of Ω are homogeneous functions of degree two in the three components of $\mathbf{k}$; the same must therefore be true of the eigenvalues.[7] Thus, if we choose a particular direction of $\mathbf{k}$ defined by a unit vector $\hat{\mathbf{k}}$, we can write

$$\omega_\nu(\mathbf{k}) = c_\nu(\hat{\mathbf{k}}) \, |\mathbf{k}|. \tag{3.49}$$

Equation (3.49) is clearly recognizable as characterizing ordinary sound waves [$c(\hat{\mathbf{k}})$ is the phase velocity]; for this reason, the three branches of the lattice vibration spectrum which have $\omega = 0$ at $\mathbf{k} = 0$ are called *acoustical branches*.

The remaining $3\mathscr{R} - 3$ branches are called *optical*. The reason for this name appears from the following considerations. Let $\eta_i^a(0;\alpha)$ be one of the acoustical solutions for $\mathbf{k} = 0$, and $\eta_i^o(0;\alpha)$ one of the other solutions at the same point of the Brillouin zone; then Eqs. (3.35) and (3.38) imply that

$$\sum_{i\alpha} M_\alpha \xi_i^a(0;\alpha)^* \xi_i^o(0;\alpha) = 0. \tag{3.50}$$

But since $\xi_i^a(0;\alpha)$ is independent of α and an arbitrary function of i, Eq. (3.50) reduces to

$$\sum_\alpha M_\alpha \xi_i^o(0;\alpha) = 0 \tag{3.51}$$

---

[6] Since $\mathbf{R}_n$ can be arbitrarily large, the expansion of the exponential can only be justified on the assumption that $\varkappa$ falls off sufficiently rapidly at large $\mathbf{R}$. This fact, incidentally, supplies a criterion for the applicability of the result we are about to obtain; viz., the wavelength $|\mathbf{k}|^{-1}$ must be large compared to the range of interatomic forces.

[7] The eigenvalues are not, however, *quadratic* in the components of $\mathbf{k}$, since they are roots of a cubic secular equation and, therefore, not analytic functions of $\mathbf{k}$.

for each i; in other words, in an optical mode at (or near) $\mathbf{k} = 0$ the center of gravity of each cell remains fixed. This implies a strong relative motion of the various atoms in the cell, and if the crystal is ionic, these modes will interact strongly with optical fields.

3.7 One-dimensional Examples

As a simple example, we consider the one-dimensional system of Fig. 3.1, in which identical atoms of mass M spaced a distance a apart are

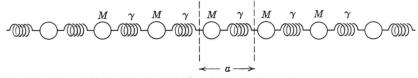

Fig. 3.1 The simplest vibrating "lattice": identical masses M are coupled to their nearest neighbors by springs of force constant γ. The dashed lines indicate a primitive cell, whose length is a.

connected by springs of force constant γ. Since the motion is one-dimensional and there is but one atom per cell, the indices α and i are superfluous. By displacing one atom a unit distance and examining the forces on it and its neighbors, we obtain the following list of nonvanishing force constants:

$$\varkappa(\mathbf{R}_n - \mathbf{R}_n) = \varkappa(0) = 2\gamma$$
$$\varkappa(\mathbf{R}_{n+1} - \mathbf{R}_n) = \varkappa(a) = -\gamma \qquad (3.52)$$
$$\varkappa(\mathbf{R}_n - \mathbf{R}_{n+1}) = \varkappa(-a) = -\gamma.$$

Therefore, from Eqs. (3.34) and (3.36),

$$\Gamma(k) = 2\gamma - \gamma e^{-ika} - \gamma e^{ika} = 4\gamma \sin^2 \frac{ka}{2} \qquad (3.53)$$

and

$$\Omega(k) = \frac{4\gamma}{M} \sin^2 \frac{ka}{2} ; \qquad (3.54)$$

since this is a one-by-one matrix, the solution is immediately[8]

$$\omega(k) = \omega_0 \left| \sin \frac{ka}{2} \right|, \qquad (3.55)$$

where

$$\omega_0{}^2 \equiv \frac{4\gamma}{M}. \qquad (3.56)$$

[8] We always take the frequency to be the positive square root of ω^2. The presence of both signs of frequency is not physically meaningful in this context; it merely signifies that both $\cos \omega t$ and $\sin \omega t$ (or equivalently $e^{i\omega t}$ and $e^{-i\omega t}$) can be used in the solution.

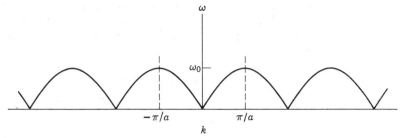

Fig. 3.2 The frequency spectrum of the "lattice" of Fig. 3.1; the dashed lines delimit the Brillouin zone.

The one-dimensional analogue of the reciprocal lattice is clearly the linear lattice of spacing $2\pi/a$, so that the first Brillouin zone is the line segment $-\pi/a < k < \pi/a$. The spectrum given by (3.55) is periodic in k, and the nonredundant part is exactly included in this segment, as shown in Fig. 3.2.

As a somewhat more complex example, consider the system of Fig. 3.3, where two different kinds of atoms are coupled to two different kinds of springs. The reader should convince himself that the only nonzero force constants are

$$\varkappa_{11}(0) = \gamma_1 + \gamma_2$$
$$\varkappa_{22}(0) = \gamma_1 + \gamma_2$$
$$\varkappa_{12}(0) = \varkappa_{21}(0) = -\gamma_1 \quad\quad (3.57)$$
$$\varkappa_{12}(a) = \varkappa_{21}(-a) = -\gamma_2$$

giving the dynamical matrix

$$\Omega = \begin{pmatrix} \dfrac{\gamma_1 + \gamma_2}{M_1} & -\dfrac{\gamma_1 + \gamma_2 e^{ika}}{(M_1 M_2)^{\frac{1}{2}}} \\[3mm] -\dfrac{\gamma_1 + \gamma_2 e^{-ika}}{(M_1 M_2)^{\frac{1}{2}}} & \dfrac{\gamma_1 + \gamma_2}{M_2} \end{pmatrix} \quad\quad (3.58)$$

The secular equation is now quadratic in ω^2 and yields two frequencies for each k; the resulting spectrum is shown in Fig. 3.4. The two branches, one acoustical and one optical, are apparent.

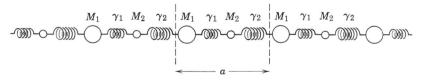

$$M_1 \quad \gamma_1 \quad M_2 \quad \gamma_2 \quad | \quad M_1 \quad \gamma_1 \quad M_2 \quad \gamma_2 \quad | \quad M_1 \quad \gamma_1 \quad M_2 \quad \gamma_2$$

Fig. 3.3 A linear chain in which two kinds of masses alternate, as do two kinds of springs.

Finally, let us examine the case where transverse, as well as longitudinal, motion is possible. If we restrict ourselves for simplicity to one
atom per cell and nearest-neighbor interaction, we obtain the following
list of force constants (cf. Fig. 3.5):

$$\varkappa_{xx}(a) = \varkappa_{xx}(-a) = -\gamma_1 \sin^2 \theta_1 - \gamma_2 \sin^2 \theta_2 \equiv -A$$
$$\varkappa_{yy}(a) = \varkappa_{yy}(-a) = -\gamma_1 \cos^2 \theta_1 - \gamma_2 \cos^2 \theta_2 \equiv -B$$
$$\varkappa_{xy}(a) = \varkappa_{yx}(-a) = \varkappa_{yx}(a) = \varkappa_{xy}(-a)$$
$$= -\gamma_1 \sin \theta_1 \cos \theta_1 + \gamma_2 \sin \theta_2 \cos \theta_2 \equiv -C \qquad (3.59)$$
$$\varkappa_{xx}(0) = 2A$$
$$\varkappa_{yy}(0) = 2B$$
$$\varkappa_{xy}(0) = \varkappa_{yx}(0) = 2C.$$

Accordingly, the matrix Ω becomes

$$\Omega = M^{-1}\begin{pmatrix} 4A \sin^2 (ka/2) & 4C \sin^2 (ka/2) \\ 4C \sin^2 (ka/2) & 4B \sin^2 (ka/2) \end{pmatrix}. \qquad (3.60)$$

The two frequencies are given by

$$\omega = 2\left[\sin \frac{ka}{2}\right]\left[\frac{A+B}{2} \pm \sqrt{\left(\frac{A-B}{2}\right)^2 + C^2}\right]^{\frac{1}{2}} M^{-\frac{1}{2}}, \qquad (3.61)$$

so that the spectrum contains two branches, each of which looks like
Fig. 3.2. Note that, unless $C = 0$, the eigenvectors of Ω, Eq. (3.60),

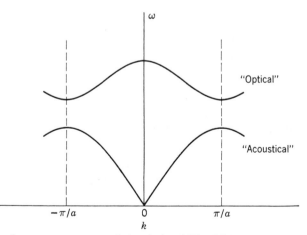

Fig. 3.4 The frequency spectrum of the chain of Fig. 3.3 has an acoustical and an
optical branch.

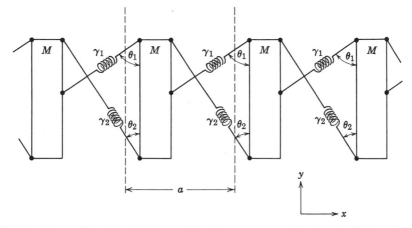

Fig. 3.5 A one-dimensional chain capable of transverse as well as longitudinal motion. It is assumed that the masses can move horizontally and vertically but are constrained not to tip.

correspond to waves which are neither pure "transverse" nor pure "longitudinal"; this is indeed the case in an anisotropic elastic medium if **k** points in an arbitrary direction.

3.8   Application to Real Crystals

Attempts to apply the foregoing theory to calculations on real crystals have in the past been severely hampered by two factors. First, it is not possible to get very far trying to obtain the $\varkappa$'s from first principles, since the electronic problem which theoretically would supply the functions $\epsilon_n(Q)$ is in fact insoluble. Secondly, it was very difficult to compare the predictions of any particular model with experiment, because until recently there was no method available for measuring the actual vibration spectrum of a solid. Instead, one had to be satisfied with results such as infrared reflection measurements (cf. Chapter 5) which primarily give information about isolated points on the dispersion curve, or specific heat measurements (cf. Chapter 4) which depend on complicated weighted averages of the vibration spectrum.

A major change in this situation occurred when it was found that by means of neutron diffraction the actual spectrum of a solid, that is, ω as a function of **k**, could be measured, and this development has renewed the interest in attempts at calculating the spectrum. Because we are still not in a position to *calculate* the force constants, it is natural to try to approximate by postulating that the interaction of each atom is only with a few near neighbors. We then have a model with a relatively small number of adjustable parameters, with which we can attempt to fit experimental spectra.

Such a method does not generally work well; one finds that, in order to obtain good agreement, so many $\varkappa$'s need to be included as adjustable parameters that the fit becomes rather meaningless. The physical reason for this is that while there are indeed strong short-range forces arising from the interpenetration of close atoms, the distortion of the atoms also gives rise to electrostatic forces of very long range. On the other hand, we note that the many $\varkappa$'s arising from electrostatic forces are not independent, but can be characterized in terms of some type of multipole expansion of which one would expect only a few terms to be important. Models which treat near-neighbor force constants as adjustable parameters and include long-range interactions in terms of relatively few additional electrostatic parameters have recently been very successful.

PROBLEMS

1. Prove that the matrix Ω is Hermitian.
2. (*a*) Find the long-wavelength velocity of sound predicted by Eq. (3.55).
   (*b*) Compare with the velocity of sound calculated from the macroscopic elastic modulus and density which the chain of Fig. 3.1 would have.
3. Find the exact eigenvalues of Eq. (3.58) for the case $\gamma_1 = \gamma_2$, $M_1 = M_2$. What is the meaning of the two branches?
4. What would be the modifications of the spectrum of Eq. (3.55) if every third atom of the chain were given the same small increase in mass?

4

Quantization of Lattice Vibrations and Calculation of Specific Heat

4.1 Introduction

Most of the lattice spectrum, whose properties were developed in the previous chapter, is characterized by wavelengths of the order of magnitude of atomic spacings, and is, therefore, not accessible to investigation by "macroscopic" experiments.[1] Exceptions are, of course, the sections very near $k = 0$ in the Brillouin zone; thus the acoustical branches are, in this vicinity, observable as sound waves, whereas the optical branches have important effects on infrared properties (cf. Sec. 5.5). But in spite of the fact that most vibrational modes have no individual macroscopic consequences, they play a crucial role in the thermal properties of the solid; the "internal energy" of thermodynamics is, in fact, nothing but the energy which a system contains in nonmacroscopic modes.

In this chapter we shall discuss the contribution of lattice vibrations to the internal energy of a crystal; but before we can do that, we must solve for the quantum-mechanical energy levels which the lattice-vibration system has. The formalism which we shall develop for this purpose will subsequently be found useful for other problems in which the quantized aspects of the lattice motion play a role.

4.2 Transformation to Normal Amplitudes

The quantum-mechanical behavior of the system described by the Hamiltonian (3.28) is determined by regarding the p's and x's as Hermitian

---

[1] See note 1 in Chapter 1 (p. 2).

operators satisfying the commutation relations

$$[p_i(n; \alpha), x_j(m; \beta)] = \frac{\hbar}{i} \delta_{ij}\, \delta_{\alpha\beta}\, \delta_{mn}, \tag{4.1}$$

with any two p's or any two x's commuting. Let us assume that the classical problem has been solved, so that we have, for each allowed $\mathbf{k}$, a set of frequencies $\omega_\lambda(\mathbf{k})$ with associated eigenvectors $\eta_i^\lambda(\mathbf{k}; \alpha)$ whose phases have been chosen so as to satisfy Eq. (3.42). Define new operators $a_\lambda(\mathbf{k})$ by

$$a_\lambda(\mathbf{k}) \equiv [2\mathcal{N}\hbar\omega_\lambda(\mathbf{k})]^{-\frac{1}{2}} \sum_{i\alpha n} M_\alpha^{-\frac{1}{2}}\eta_i^\lambda(\mathbf{k}; \alpha)^* e^{-i\mathbf{k}\cdot\mathbf{R}_n}$$

$$\times [p_i(n; \alpha) - iM_\alpha\omega_\lambda(\mathbf{k})x_i(n; \alpha)]. \tag{4.2}$$

These can be considered as the amplitudes of excitation of the normal modes $\mathbf{k}\lambda$, in that classically the (complex) dynamical variables $a_\lambda(\mathbf{k})$ would have a time-dependence of the form $\exp[-i\omega_\lambda(\mathbf{k})t]$.

The a's satisfy the commutation relations

$$[a_\lambda(\mathbf{k}), a_\mu^\dagger(\mathbf{k}')] = \delta_{\lambda\mu}\, \delta_{\mathbf{kk}'}; \tag{4.3}$$

$$[a_\lambda(\mathbf{k}), a_\mu(\mathbf{k}')] = [a_\lambda^\dagger(\mathbf{k}), a_\mu^\dagger(\mathbf{k}')] = 0. \tag{4.4}$$

To prove the first one, note that

$$[\{p_i(n; \alpha) - iM_\alpha\omega_\lambda(\mathbf{k})x_i(n; \alpha)\}, \{p_j(m; \beta) + iM_\beta\omega_\mu(\mathbf{k}')x_j(m; \beta)\}]$$

$$= \hbar M_\alpha[\omega_\lambda(\mathbf{k}) + \omega_\mu(\mathbf{k}')]\, \delta_{ij}\, \delta_{\alpha\beta}\, \delta_{nm}. \tag{4.5}$$

Therefore

$$[a_\lambda(\mathbf{k}), a_\mu^\dagger(\mathbf{k}')] = \frac{1}{2\mathcal{N}}[\omega_\lambda(\mathbf{k})\omega_\mu(\mathbf{k}')]^{-\frac{1}{2}}[\omega_\lambda(\mathbf{k}) + \omega_\mu(\mathbf{k}')]$$

$$\times \sum_{i\alpha n} \eta_i^\lambda(\mathbf{k}; \alpha)^* \eta_i^\mu(\mathbf{k}'; \alpha) e^{i(\mathbf{k}'-\mathbf{k})\cdot\mathbf{R}_n}$$

$$= \tfrac{1}{2}[\omega_\lambda(\mathbf{k})\omega_\mu(\mathbf{k}')]^{-\frac{1}{2}}[\omega_\lambda(\mathbf{k}) + \omega_\mu(\mathbf{k}')]\, \delta_{\mathbf{kk}'}$$

$$\times \sum_{i\alpha} \eta_i^\lambda(\mathbf{k}; \alpha)^* \eta_i^\mu(\mathbf{k}; \alpha)$$

$$= \delta_{\mathbf{kk}'}\, \delta_{\lambda\mu}. \tag{4.6}$$

The other two relations are proved in Problem 1.

From these commutation relations (which the a's were specifically designed to satisfy) the following immediate conclusions can be drawn.

If we define Hermitian operators

$$N_\lambda(\mathbf{k}) \equiv a_\lambda^\dagger(\mathbf{k})a_\lambda(\mathbf{k}), \tag{4.7}$$

one for each normal mode, we find that any two N's commute, so there exists a complete set of simultaneous eigenstates of all of them. The relations

$$N_\lambda(\mathbf{k})a_\lambda^\dagger(\mathbf{k}) = a_\lambda^\dagger(\mathbf{k})[N_\lambda(\mathbf{k}) + 1]$$
$$N_\lambda(\mathbf{k})a_\lambda(\mathbf{k}) = a_\lambda(\mathbf{k})[N_\lambda(\mathbf{k}) - 1], \tag{4.8}$$

which follow from Eqs. (4.3), (4.4), and (4.7), then imply that $a_\lambda^\dagger(\mathbf{k})$ applied to an eigenstate of $N_\lambda(\mathbf{k})$ will raise the eigenvalue by unity whereas $a_\lambda(\mathbf{k})$ will lower it by the same amount. It can further be shown in the usual manner that the eigenvalues of each $N_\lambda(\mathbf{k})$ are the non-negative integers, and that the matrix element of a or $a^\dagger$ between eigenstates of N which it connects is equal to the square root of the larger eigenvalue.[2] Of course the introduction of the a's and $a^\dagger$'s has so far been a purely kinematical transformation of variables; the importance of the particular choice (4.2) will appear in the next section.

4.3 Hamiltonian in Terms of Normal Amplitudes

As shown in Problem 2, the relation (4.2) can be inverted to give

$$p_i(n;\alpha) = \sum_{\mathbf{k}\lambda} \left[\frac{M_\alpha \hbar \omega_\lambda(\mathbf{k})}{2\mathcal{N}}\right]^{1/2}$$
$$\times [a_\lambda(\mathbf{k})\eta_i^\lambda(\mathbf{k};\alpha)e^{i\mathbf{k}\cdot\mathbf{R}_n} + a_\lambda^\dagger(\mathbf{k})\eta_i^\lambda(\mathbf{k};\alpha)^*e^{-i\mathbf{k}\cdot\mathbf{R}_n}], \tag{4.9}$$

$$x_i(n;\alpha) = i\sum_{\mathbf{k}\lambda} \left[\frac{\hbar}{2\mathcal{N}M_\alpha\omega_\lambda(\mathbf{k})}\right]^{1/2}$$
$$\times [a_\lambda(\mathbf{k})\eta_i^\lambda(\mathbf{k};\alpha)e^{i\mathbf{k}\cdot\mathbf{R}_n} - a_\lambda^\dagger(\mathbf{k})\eta_i^\lambda(\mathbf{k};\alpha)^*e^{-i\mathbf{k}\cdot\mathbf{R}_n}]. \tag{4.10}$$

Substituting the first into the kinetic energy term of Eq. (3.28), we obtain

$$\frac{1}{2}\sum_{i\alpha n}\frac{[p_i(n;\alpha)]^2}{M_\alpha} = \frac{\hbar}{4\mathcal{N}}\sum_{i\alpha n}\sum_{\mathbf{k}\lambda}\sum_{\mathbf{k}'\mu}[\omega_\lambda(\mathbf{k})\omega_\mu(\mathbf{k}')]^{1/2}$$
$$\times [a_\lambda(\mathbf{k})\eta_i^\lambda(\mathbf{k};\alpha)e^{i\mathbf{k}\cdot\mathbf{R}_n} + a_\lambda^\dagger(\mathbf{k})\eta_i^\lambda(\mathbf{k};\alpha)^*e^{-i\mathbf{k}\cdot\mathbf{R}_n}]$$
$$\times [a_\mu(\mathbf{k}')\eta_i^\mu(\mathbf{k}';\alpha)e^{i\mathbf{k}'\cdot\mathbf{R}_n} + a_\mu^\dagger(\mathbf{k}')\eta_i^\mu(\mathbf{k}';\alpha)^*e^{-i\mathbf{k}'\cdot\mathbf{R}_n}]. \tag{4.11}$$

---

[2] The reader is assumed to be familiar with these relations from the elementary theory of the harmonic oscillator.

The sum over n takes the form (2.24), as a result of which a typical cross-term (i.e., a term with one a and one $a^\dagger$) reduces as follows:

$$\sum_{i\alpha n} [\omega_\lambda(\mathbf{k})\omega_\mu(\mathbf{k}')]^{1/2} a_\lambda(\mathbf{k})\eta_i^\lambda(\mathbf{k};\alpha)e^{i\mathbf{k}\cdot\mathbf{R}_n} a_\mu^\dagger(\mathbf{k}')\eta_i^\mu(\mathbf{k}';\alpha)^* e^{-i\mathbf{k}'\cdot\mathbf{R}_n}$$

$$= [\omega_\lambda(\mathbf{k})\omega_\mu(\mathbf{k})]^{1/2} a_\lambda(\mathbf{k})a_\mu^\dagger(\mathbf{k})\mathcal{N}\,\delta_{\mathbf{k}\mathbf{k}'} \sum_{i\alpha} \eta_i^\mu(\mathbf{k};\alpha)^* \eta_i^\lambda(\mathbf{k};\alpha)$$

$$= \omega_\lambda(\mathbf{k})a_\lambda(\mathbf{k})a_\lambda^\dagger(\mathbf{k})\mathcal{N}\,\delta_{\mathbf{k}\mathbf{k}'}\,\delta_{\lambda\mu}, \tag{4.12}$$

where we have used the orthogonality of the η's, Eq. (3.38). On the other hand a term with, say, two a's contains the sum

$$\sum_n e^{i\mathbf{k}\cdot\mathbf{R}_n}e^{i\mathbf{k}'\cdot\mathbf{R}_n} = \mathcal{N}\,\delta_{\mathbf{k},-\mathbf{k}'}, \tag{4.13}$$

so that, with the use of Eqs. (3.41) and (3.42),

$$\sum_{i\alpha n} [\omega_\lambda(\mathbf{k})\omega_\mu(\mathbf{k}')]^{1/2} a_\lambda(\mathbf{k})\eta_i^\lambda(\mathbf{k};\alpha)e^{i\mathbf{k}\cdot\mathbf{R}_n} a_\mu(\mathbf{k}')\eta_i^\mu(\mathbf{k}';\alpha)e^{i\mathbf{k}'\cdot\mathbf{R}_n}$$

$$= [\omega_\lambda(\mathbf{k})\omega_\mu(-\mathbf{k})]^{1/2} a_\lambda(\mathbf{k})a_\mu(-\mathbf{k})\mathcal{N}\,\delta_{\mathbf{k},-\mathbf{k}'} \sum_{i\alpha} \eta_i^\lambda(\mathbf{k};\alpha)\eta_i^\mu(-\mathbf{k};\alpha)$$

$$= \omega_\lambda(\mathbf{k})a_\lambda(\mathbf{k})a_\lambda(-\mathbf{k})\mathcal{N}\,\delta_{\mathbf{k},-\mathbf{k}'}\,\delta_{\lambda\mu}. \tag{4.14}$$

The final form for the kinetic energy thus becomes

$$\frac{1}{2}\sum_{i\alpha n} \frac{[p_i(n;\alpha)]^2}{M_\alpha} = \frac{1}{4}\sum_{k\lambda} \hbar\omega_\lambda(\mathbf{k})$$

$$\times [a_\lambda(\mathbf{k})a_\lambda(-\mathbf{k}) + a_\lambda^\dagger(\mathbf{k})a_\lambda^\dagger(-\mathbf{k}) + a_\lambda^\dagger(\mathbf{k})a_\lambda(\mathbf{k}) + a_\lambda(\mathbf{k})a_\lambda^\dagger(\mathbf{k})]. \tag{4.15}$$

The reduction of the potential energy is a little more complicated. It is convenient first to change the summation variables in Eq. (3.18) and write

$$V = \frac{1}{2} \sum_{nmij\alpha\beta} \varkappa_{\alpha i;\,\beta j}(\mathbf{R}_m)x_i(n+m;\alpha)x_j(n;\beta) \tag{4.16}$$

where $n+m$ stands for the vector $\mathbf{R}_n + \mathbf{R}_m$. If we now substitute Eq. (4.10) for the x's, the summation over n can be immediately performed, whereas the summation over m converts the $\varkappa$'s into Ω's according to Eqs. (3.34) and (3.36). Recalling that the η's are eigenvectors of Ω, so that

$$\sum_{\beta j} \Omega_{\alpha i;\,\beta j}(\mathbf{k})\eta_j^\lambda(\mathbf{k};\beta) = [\omega_\lambda(\mathbf{k})]^2\eta_i^\lambda(\mathbf{k};\alpha), \tag{4.17}$$

we find that the potential energy now reduces in the same way that the kinetic did, with the result

$$V = -\frac{1}{4}\sum_{k\lambda} \hbar\omega_\lambda(\mathbf{k})[a_\lambda(\mathbf{k})a_\lambda(-\mathbf{k}) + a_\lambda^\dagger(\mathbf{k})a_\lambda^\dagger(-\mathbf{k})$$

$$- a_\lambda^\dagger(\mathbf{k})a_\lambda(\mathbf{k}) - a_\lambda(\mathbf{k})a_\lambda^\dagger(\mathbf{k})]. \tag{4.18}$$

Combining this with Eq. (4.15), we see that terms containing opposite **k**'s vanish, so that

$$H = \frac{1}{2} \sum_{\mathbf{k}\lambda} \hbar\omega_\lambda(\mathbf{k})[a_\lambda^\dagger(\mathbf{k})a_\lambda(\mathbf{k}) + a_\lambda(\mathbf{k})a_\lambda^\dagger(\mathbf{k})], \tag{4.19}$$

which with the help of Eqs. (4.3) and (4.7) reduces to

$$H = \sum_{\mathbf{k}\lambda} \hbar\omega_\lambda(\mathbf{k})[N_\lambda(\mathbf{k}) + \tfrac{1}{2}]. \tag{4.20}$$

At this point the kinematical spadework of introducing the a's in the particular form (4.2) has paid off. The resulting Hamiltonian commutes with all the N's, and its eigenvalues are directly given by Eq. (4.20) if to each N we assign an arbitrary non-negative integer.

4.4   Translation Behavior of State Vectors

We have found in the previous section a set of simultaneous eigenstates of H and all the $N_\lambda(\mathbf{k})$'s.[3] On the other hand, since H commutes with all the translations of the lattice, it must also be possible to find a set of simultaneous eigenstates of H and all the $\mathscr{T}$'s. We shall now prove that these two sets are actually the same.

The effect of a translation operator on the x and p operators is given by

$$\mathscr{T}_m x_i(n; \alpha)\mathscr{T}_m^{-1} = x_i(n + m; \alpha)$$
$$\mathscr{T}_m p_i(n; \alpha)\mathscr{T}_m^{-1} = p_i(n + m; \alpha), \tag{4.21}$$

where $\mathscr{T}_m$ is short for $\mathscr{T}(\mathbf{R}_m)$. Applying these equations to (4.2) yields

$$\mathscr{T}_m a_\lambda(\mathbf{k})\mathscr{T}_m^{-1} = [2\mathcal{N}\hbar\omega_\lambda(\mathbf{k})]^{-\frac{1}{2}} \sum_{i\alpha n} M_\alpha^{-\frac{1}{2}}\eta_i^\lambda(\mathbf{k}; \alpha)^* e^{-i\mathbf{k}\cdot\mathbf{R}_n}$$
$$\times [p_i(n + m; \alpha) - iM_\alpha\omega_\lambda(\mathbf{k})x_i(n + m; \alpha)]$$
$$= e^{i\mathbf{k}\cdot\mathbf{R}_m}a_\lambda(\mathbf{k}) \tag{4.22}$$

by a change of summation index; and similarly

$$\mathscr{T}_m a_\lambda^\dagger(\mathbf{k})\mathscr{T}_m^{-1} = e^{-i\mathbf{k}\cdot\mathbf{R}_m}a_\lambda^\dagger(\mathbf{k}). \tag{4.23}$$

It follows that

$$\mathscr{T}_m N_\lambda(\mathbf{k})\mathscr{T}_m^{-1} = \mathscr{T}_m a_\lambda^\dagger(\mathbf{k})\mathscr{T}_m^{-1}\mathscr{T}_m a_\lambda(\mathbf{k})\mathscr{T}_m^{-1} = N_\lambda(\mathbf{k}), \tag{4.24}$$

so that every $\mathscr{T}$ commutes with every N. Therefore, it is possible to diagonalize the $\mathscr{T}$'s simultaneously with the N's; and since there is only one

---

[3] We can say that we have "found" the states in spite of not having written any explicit wave functions; for we know how the a's and $a^\dagger$'s act on them, and also how to write any operator of interest in terms of a's and $a^\dagger$'s.

state for a given set of eigenvalues of the N's it must also be an eigenstate of all the $\mathcal{T}$'s.

It is interesting to investigate further what the eigenvalue of a particular $\mathcal{T}$ is for such a state. Consider first the state, which we denote by $|0\rangle$, in which all the N's vanish. We know it to be an eigenstate of all $\mathcal{T}$'s, so that there must exist a vector $\mathcal{K}_0$ such that

$$\mathcal{T}_m |0\rangle = e^{-i\mathcal{K}_0 \cdot \mathbf{R}_m} |0\rangle \tag{4.25}$$

for any $\mathbf{R}_m$. Now except for normalization, a general state can be expressed as[4]

$$|N_{\lambda_1}(\mathbf{k}_1), N_{\lambda_2}(\mathbf{k}_2), \ldots\rangle = \left\{\prod_{\mathbf{k}\lambda} [a_\lambda{}^\dagger(\mathbf{k})]^{N_\lambda(\mathbf{k})}\right\} |0\rangle; \tag{4.26}$$

hence, from Eq. (4.23),

$$\mathcal{T}_m |N_{\lambda_1}(\mathbf{k}_1), \ldots\rangle = \exp\left\{-i\left[\mathcal{K}_0 + \sum_{\mathbf{k}\lambda} N_\lambda(\mathbf{k})\mathbf{k}\right] \cdot \mathbf{R}_m\right\} |N_{\lambda_1}(\mathbf{k}_1), \ldots\rangle. \tag{4.27}$$

4.5   Crystal Momentum and "Phonons"

We have seen in Sec. 2.3 that if a state $|\psi\rangle$ is a simultaneous eigenstate of all the lattice translation operators, the eigenvalues of all these operators are related by

$$\mathcal{T}_m |\psi\rangle = e^{-i\mathcal{K}\cdot\mathbf{R}_m} |\psi\rangle; \tag{4.28}$$

in other words, one vector $\mathcal{K}$ specifies all the eigenvalues. The quantity

$$\mathcal{P} \equiv \hbar\mathcal{K} \tag{4.29}$$

is called the *crystal momentum* of such a state. Note that if $\mathcal{K}$ is replaced by $\mathcal{K} + \mathbf{K}$, where $\mathbf{K}$ is a reciprocal lattice vector, the eigenvalues of the $\mathcal{T}$'s are unchanged; that is, $\mathcal{K}$ is indeterminate to within a reciprocal lattice vector, so that we lose no generality in restricting its domain to the Brillouin zone. Correspondingly, $\mathcal{P}$ becomes restricted to a domain which is identical to the Brillouin zone except that the scale is multiplied by $\hbar$ in all directions.

For the state $|N_{\lambda_1}(k_1), N_{\lambda_2}(k_2), \ldots\rangle$ we have from Eq. (4.20)

$$E = E_0 + \frac{1}{2}\sum_{\mathbf{k}\lambda} \hbar\omega_\lambda(\mathbf{k}) + \sum_{\mathbf{k}\lambda} N_\lambda(\mathbf{k})\hbar\omega_\lambda(\mathbf{k}), \tag{4.30}$$

and from (4.27)

$$\mathcal{P} = \hbar\mathcal{K}_0 + \sum_{\mathbf{k}\lambda} N_\lambda(\mathbf{k})\hbar\mathbf{k}. \tag{4.31}$$

[4] The symbol $|N_{\lambda_1}(\mathbf{k}_1), N_{\lambda_2}(\mathbf{k}_2), \ldots\rangle$ represents the state in which the N-operator of mode $\mathbf{k}_1\lambda_1$ has the eigenvalue $N_{\lambda_1}(\mathbf{k}_1)$, etc.

These two equations suggest the following "particle language": we describe the state as one containing $N_{\lambda_1}(\mathbf{k}_1)$ "phonons" in the mode $\mathbf{k}_1\lambda_1$, $N_{\lambda_2}(\mathbf{k}_2)$ phonons in the mode $\mathbf{k}_2\lambda_2$, and so on. Equations (4.30) and (4.31) can then be put into words by saying that *a phonon in mode* $\mathbf{k}\lambda$ *has energy* $\hbar\omega_\lambda(\mathbf{k})$ *and crystal momentum* $\hbar\mathbf{k}$. It is apparent that the operators $a_\lambda{}^\dagger(\mathbf{k})$ and $a_\lambda(\mathbf{k})$ have the property of increasing or decreasing the number of phonons in mode $\mathbf{k}\lambda$ by unity; they are, therefore, called *phonon creation operators* and *phonon destruction operators*, respectively.

Since all the $N_\lambda(\mathbf{k})$'s are constants of the motion, it follows that if at a particular time the number of phonons in each mode is known, these numbers will not change with time. It seems like a trivial corollary to this that the total crystal momentum is constant in time; but in fact the last statement has considerably more generality than the premise from which it was derived. Suppose, for example, that we add to the Hamiltonian the next higher term of the Taylor series whose beginning is given by Eq. (3.18), that is, a term cubic in the displacements. As shown in Problem 3, this gives rise to transitions (described as *phonon-phonon scattering*) in which a number of the N's simultaneously change. On the other hand, the presence of anharmonicity in the interatomic forces does not affect the periodicity of the crystal, so that all the $\mathscr{T}$'s are still constants of the motion and the crystal momentum remains conserved.

The treatment of this section gives no information on the constants E_0 and $\mathscr{K}_0$ which appear in Eqs. (4.30) and (4.31). This is to be expected, since we have said nothing about any nonvibrational degrees of freedom; other fields (such as electrons and electromagnetic waves) will contribute their share to both the energy and the crystal momentum of the system. If the Hamiltonian is made to include coupling terms between these various fields, the crystal momentum of each one may change, but the *total* crystal momentum must remain constant if the total Hamiltonian commutes with the translations of the lattice.

4.6   The Internal Energy

If the energy levels of a system are numbered by a parameter ν, and if the energy of the state ν is denoted by E_ν, then the probability that the system is in a particular state is given by

$$p_\nu = \frac{e^{-\beta E_\nu}}{\sum_\mu e^{-\beta E_\mu}} \tag{4.32}$$

where

$$\beta \equiv \frac{1}{KT}, \tag{4.33}$$

K being Boltzmann's constant and T the absolute temperature. Therefore, the expectation value of the energy of the system is

$$U \equiv \sum_v p_v E_v = - \frac{\partial}{\partial \beta} \log \sum_v e^{-\beta E_v}. \tag{4.34}$$

The energy levels of the lattice vibration system are specified by phonon occupation numbers $N_\lambda(\mathbf{k})$ for each $\mathbf{k}\lambda$, and the corresponding energies are $\sum_{\mathbf{k}\lambda} [N_\lambda(\mathbf{k}) + \tfrac{1}{2}]\hbar\omega_\lambda(\mathbf{k})$. Therefore

$$\sum_v e^{-\beta E_v} = \sum_{\text{each } N=0}^{\infty} \exp\left\{ -\beta \sum_{\mathbf{k}\lambda} [N_\lambda(\mathbf{k}) + \tfrac{1}{2}]\hbar\omega_\lambda(\mathbf{k}) \right\}$$

$$= \prod_{\mathbf{k}\lambda} \sum_{N=0}^{\infty} e^{-\beta[N+\frac{1}{2}]\hbar\omega_\lambda(\mathbf{k})} = \prod_{\mathbf{k}\lambda} \tfrac{1}{2} \operatorname{csch} [\tfrac{1}{2}\beta\hbar\omega_\lambda(\mathbf{k})], \tag{4.35}$$

which upon differentiation according to Eq. (4.34) yields

$$U = \sum_{\mathbf{k}\lambda} \frac{\hbar\omega_\lambda(\mathbf{k})}{2} \coth \frac{\beta\hbar\omega_\lambda(\mathbf{k})}{2}$$

$$= \sum_{\mathbf{k}\lambda} \frac{\hbar\omega_\lambda(\mathbf{k})}{2} + \sum_{\mathbf{k}\lambda} \frac{\hbar\omega_\lambda(\mathbf{k})}{e^{\beta\hbar\omega_\lambda(\mathbf{k})} - 1}. \tag{4.36}$$

In the last expression the "zero-point energy," which is independent of temperature, has been separated from the part of the energy which vanishes when T goes to zero.

The evaluation of (4.36) for the case of high temperatures is especially easy. Let T be large enough so that $\beta\hbar\omega_\lambda(k) \ll 1$ for all modes $\mathbf{k}\lambda$. Expanding the exponential then gives

$$U = U_0 + \sum_{\mathbf{k}\lambda} KT = U_0 + 3\mathscr{R}\mathscr{N} KT, \tag{4.37}$$

where U_0 is the temperature-independent part of (4.36). The specific heat at constant volume is obtained by differentiating U with respect to T. Thus, Eq. (4.37) predicts that at high temperatures the specific heat is independent of temperature and equal to $3K$ times the number of atoms in the crystal. This result, which is equivalent to the assumption of *equipartition* (that is, the presence of energy KT in each vibrational mode) is known as the law of Dulong and Petit.

Except in this simple limit, it is convenient to replace the sum in Eq. (4.36) by an integral.[5] We then obtain

$$U = U_0 + \int_0^\infty \frac{\rho(\omega)\hbar\omega \, d\omega}{e^{\beta\hbar\omega} - 1} \tag{4.38}$$

where $\rho(\omega) \, d\omega$ is the number of modes in a frequency interval $d\omega$ around ω.

---

[5] See Sec. 4.12 for discussion of this point.

4.7 Density of Modes in Frequency

Equation (4.38) shows that the internal energy is determined by the density of modes $\rho(\omega)$, which is, of course, a sum of the contributions of the various branches of the vibration spectrum; we shall limit our consideration for the moment to one branch. The locus of all points in the Brillouin zone corresponding to a particular frequency is called a *constant-frequency surface*. Now let us imagine two constant-frequency surfaces drawn, one for frequency ω, the other for $\omega + d\omega$. The spacing between them is then $d\omega/|\nabla_\mathbf{k}\omega|$, where $\nabla_\mathbf{k}\omega$ is the gradient of ω in $\mathbf{k}$-space. Needless to say, the spacing varies from point to point even on the same surface. The volume of $\mathbf{k}$-space included between the two surfaces is

$$d\omega \int \frac{dS}{|\nabla_\mathbf{k}(\omega)|} \equiv d\omega \int \frac{dS}{v}, \qquad (4.39)$$

where the integral is over the constant-frequency surface. The notation v for $|\nabla_\mathbf{k}\omega|$ is based on the fact that the gradient is, by a well-known theorem, equal to the *group velocity* of a wavepacket centered at the point $\mathbf{k}$.

We know from Chapter 2 that, for a particular branch of the spectrum, the density of allowed values of $\mathbf{k}$ in the zone is $V/(2\pi)^3$. Accordingly, we obtain for the number of modes between ω and $\omega + d\omega$

$$\rho(\omega)\, d\omega = d\omega \frac{V}{(2\pi)^3} \int \frac{dS}{v}, \qquad (4.40)$$

or
$$\rho(\omega) = \frac{V}{(2\pi)^3} \int \frac{dS}{v}. \qquad (4.41)$$

Equation (4.41) shows that, since the area of the frequency surface and the velocity v are smooth functions of ω, the function $\rho(\omega)$ will generally be a smoothly varying one, except that special examination has to be given to values of ω whose surfaces include "critical points," that is, points at which $v = 0$. If $\omega(\mathbf{k})$ were a differentiable function of $\mathbf{k}$, we could state immediately that since the frequency range of a branch is bounded, each branch must contain at least two critical points—namely, its maximum and its minimum.

The situation is not, however, quite so simple. We recall that the frequencies are obtained by diagonalization of the $3\mathscr{R} \times 3\mathscr{R}$ matrix Ω, Eq. (3.37). As $\mathbf{k}$ varies, the matrix elements of Ω vary analytically, from which we may conclude that its eigenvalues vary analytically (we are assuming that two branches of the spectrum never cross; more discussion of this point will be given in Chapter 6 in connection with electronic energy bands). The eigenvalue of Ω is, however, not ω but ω^2, so that at a minimum or a maximum we may write

$$|\nabla_k(\omega^2)| = 2\omega v = 0, \qquad (4.42)$$

from which we conclude that $v = 0$ at a minimum or a maximum provided ω is not zero, that is, except at the bottom of the acoustical branches.

The difficulty at $\omega = 0$ could be avoided if instead of discussing $\rho(\omega)$, we discussed the density of modes per unit square frequency. The latter quantity, which we denote by $\sigma(\omega^2)$, is defined by

$$\sigma(\omega^2)\, d(\omega^2) = \rho(\omega)\, d\omega, \qquad (4.43)$$

or
$$\rho(\omega) = 2\omega\sigma(\omega). \qquad (4.44)$$

It is clear that for $\omega \neq 0$ the *qualitative* behavior of ρ and σ will be the same, so that the distinction need not, for our purposes, be made. Our procedure in the following will be to limit ourselves *temporarily* to optical branches or critical points in acoustical branches other than the minimum.

4.8 Saddle Points

Near a critical point, ω is a quadratic function of the components of **k** measured from the critical point as origin. With the coordinate axes of **k** chosen so as to eliminate cross-terms, the expression is

$$\omega - \omega_c = Ak_1^2 + Bk_2^2 + Ck_3^2, \qquad (4.45)$$

where ω_c is the frequency *at* the critical point. We may now classify the point according to the number of coefficients A, B, C which are negative. Thus a type 0 critical point is a minimum and a type 3 point is a maximum. Types 1 and 2 are *saddle points;* in leaving them the frequency increases in some directions and decreases in others.

The existence of saddle points is topologically required by the periodicity of $\omega(\mathbf{k})$ in the reciprocal lattice, which in turn follows directly from the periodicity of the matrix elements of Ω, Eqs. (3.36) and (3.34). The general theorem is the following: a function of N variables which is periodic in all of them must have at least $C_n{}^N$ critical points of type n in each N-dimensional primitive cell, where

$$C_n{}^N \equiv \frac{N!}{n!(N-n)!}$$

is the binomial coefficient. Thus, for example, a doubly periodic function must have at least one minimum, one maximum, and two saddle points of type 1 (there are no other types of saddle points in two dimensions); a triply periodic function such as $\omega(\mathbf{k})$ must have, in addition to a minimum and a maximum, at least three saddle points of type 1 and three of type 2.

We shall now prove this theorem. Let the function be $F(x_1, x_2, \ldots x_N)$, periodic in each independent variable; let $S(N; n)$ be the minimum number of critical points of type n which such a function can have. Suppose for the moment that x_N is fixed; then F becomes a periodic function of $N - 1$ variables, and must by definition have no fewer than $S(N - 1; n)$ critical points of type n. We further assume that no two critical points ever coincide, that is, that at points where all first derivatives of F vanish some of the second derivatives do not fortuitously vanish as well.

Consider now *one* of these $S(N - 1; n)$ critical points of type n, and examine the value of the function F there as the Nth variable x_N is varied through *its* period. Clearly, this set of values must have a minimum. But the position of the minimum is a critical point of type n in the N-dimensional space, since at that point all N first derivatives vanish, and the additional second derivative is positive.

Analogous reasoning shows that a type n critical point in N-dimensional space will also arise from each point of type $n - 1$ in the $(N - 1)$-dimensional cross-section, namely, at the position where F has its *maximum* value. Since no two of these can coincide, we get for the least possible number of points of type n

$$S(N; n) = S(N - 1; n) + S(N - 1; n - 1). \qquad (4.46)$$

Equation (4.46) is the familiar relation satisfied by the binomial coefficients. Noting further that a one-dimensional function must have at least one minimum and one maximum, we can write

$$S(1; 0) = 1, \qquad S(1; 1) = 1. \qquad (4.47)$$

With this initial condition and Eq. (4.46), the equality of the S's to the binomial coefficients is established.

4.9   Values of the Frequency at Critical Points

The fact that the function $\omega(\mathbf{k})$ has at least eight critical points does not necessarily mean that there are eight separate "critical frequency surfaces," since more than one point may correspond to a single value of ω. In particular, it is possible for all points of one type to have the same frequency: thus in three dimensions we could have as few as four critical frequencies ω_0, ω_1, ω_2, and ω_3. No further coincidence of frequencies is possible, however. For considering the (type 1) saddle point in a two-dimensional cross-section, its minimum will generate a type 1 point in three dimensions, whereas its maximum will generate a type 2 point. Since the maximum must be larger than the minimum, we have (extending the same argument to other types)

$$\omega_0 < \omega_1 < \omega_2 < \omega_3. \tag{4.48}$$

Thus, in the simplest case we have not only the obvious fact that the maximum frequency ω_3 is larger than the minimum frequency ω_0, but also that the two types of saddle points are appropriately ordered in between.

4.10   Density of Modes near Critical Frequencies

We can choose axes $k_1 k_2 k_3$ with origin at the critical point such that the coefficients A and B in Eq. (4.45) have the same sign; let us further change the scale of k_2, if necessary, so as to make $A = B$. Defining cylindrical coordinates $r = (k_1{}^2 + k_2{}^2)^{\frac{1}{2}}$, $\theta = \arctan k_2/k_1$, and $k_z = k_3$, we obtain

$$\omega - \omega_c = Ar^2 + Ck_3{}^2; \tag{4.49}$$

whereas the density of modes becomes

$$\rho(\omega) = \frac{\lambda V}{(2\pi)^3} \int \frac{dS}{v}, \tag{4.50}$$

where λ is the scaling factor which was introduced to make the coefficients of k_1 and k_2 equal. The classification of critical points is then the following:

Type 0. $A > 0$, $C > 0$. For $\omega > \omega_0$, the frequency surface is an ellipsoid; for $\omega < \omega_0$, there is no surface.

Type 1. $A > 0$, $C < 0$. For $\omega < \omega_1$, the surface is a hyperboloid of two sheets; for $\omega > \omega_1$, it is a hyperboloid of one sheet.

Type 2. $A < 0$, $C > 0$. For $\omega < \omega_2$, the surface is a hyperboloid of one sheet; for $\omega > \omega_2$, it is a hyperboloid of two sheets.

Type 3. $A < 0$, $C < 0$. For $\omega < \omega_3$, the surface is an ellipsoid; for $\omega > \omega_3$, there is no surface.

To examine the behavior of the integral (4.50), we use the fact that the frequency surface is now a figure of revolution. Consider an element of surface between k_3 and $k_3 + dk_3$, as in Fig. 4.1. Its area is given by

$$dS = \frac{2\pi r\, dk_3}{\cos \gamma}, \tag{4.51}$$

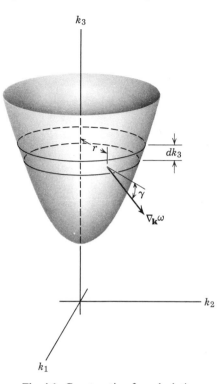

Fig. 4.1 Construction for calculating
density of modes near a critical point.

where γ is the angle between the normal and the k_1k_2-plane. Since the
normal is in the direction of $\nabla_{\mathbf{k}}\omega$, we have

$$\cos \gamma = \frac{|\partial\omega/\partial r|}{|\nabla_{\mathbf{k}}\omega|} = \frac{2\,|A|\,r}{v}, \tag{4.52}$$

so that

$$\frac{dS}{v} = \frac{\pi\,dk_3}{|A|} \tag{4.53}$$

and

$$\rho(\omega) = \frac{\lambda V}{8\pi^2\,|A|} \int dk_3. \tag{4.54}$$

In other words, $\rho(\omega)$ is proportional to the extent of the frequency surface
in the k_3-direction. As a result, the behavior of $\rho(\omega)$ near critical points is
as follows:

Type 0.   The surface extends from $k_3 = -[(\omega - \omega_0)/C]^{1/2}$ to $k_3 = +[(\omega - \omega_0)/C]^{1/2}$. Thus $\rho(\omega)$ varies as $(\omega - \omega_0)^{1/2}$, rising from $\omega = \omega_0$
with infinite slope (Fig. 4.2*a*).

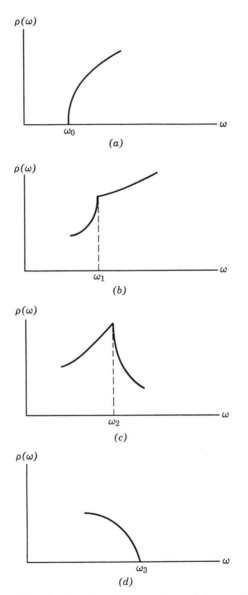

Fig. 4.2 Behavior of the density of modes near (*a*) a minimum, (*b*) a type 1 saddle point, (*c*) a type 2 saddle point, (*d*) a maximum.

Type 1. For $\omega < \omega_1$ the surface extends from $k_3 = -\infty$ to $k_3 = +\infty$ *except* for a gap from $k_3 = -[(\omega_1 - \omega)/|C|]^{\frac{1}{2}}$ to $k_3 = +[(\omega_1 - \omega)/|C|]^{\frac{1}{2}}$; for $\omega > \omega_1$ there is no gap. The infinite extent of the hyperboloids is not relevant, since Eq. (4.45) is only correct near the critical point; in fact the outer portions of the surface are finite and smoothly varying. Therefore, $\rho(\omega)$ comes into ω_1 from below with infinite slope, but leaves with finite slope (Fig. 4.2*b*).

Type 2. Analogous reasoning shows that $\rho(\omega)$ comes into ω_2 with finite slope, then drops with infinite slope (Fig. 4.2*c*).

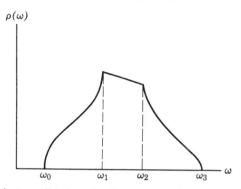

Fig. 4.3 The simplest possible branch of a spectrum has four critical frequencies in the order 0, 1, 2, 3.

Type 3. The maximum behaves analogously to the minimum, but with reversed frequency scale, so that $\rho(\omega)$ varies as $(\omega_3 - \omega)^{\frac{1}{2}}$ below the maximum, and is zero above (Fig. 4.2*d*).

We saw in Sec. 4.9 that the simplest possible branch of the spectrum has four critical frequencies arranged according to (4.48). The function $\rho(\omega)$ would, in that case, have the qualitative appearance of Fig. 4.3. If the branch has more critical frequencies, or if several branches are superimposed, the corresponding graph can become much more scalloped. It remains true, however, that at each critical frequency $\rho(\omega)$ will have a kink on one side of which its slope is infinite; by noting whether the infinity is positive or negative, and whether it occurs on the low or high side of the critical frequency, the type of critical point can always be determined.

4.11   Minimum of Acoustical Branches

At the bottom of an acoustical branch, the frequency is *not* a quadratic function of **k**, but is given rather by Eq. (3.49). This means that v depends on angle only; any two frequency surfaces are (for a particular branch) geometrically similar to each other, with the ratio of linear dimensions in **k**-space equal to the ratio of frequencies. It follows that the integral (4.41) will be proportional to the square of the frequency:

$$\rho(\omega) = \text{const. } \omega^2. \tag{4.55}$$

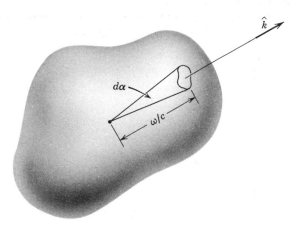

Fig. 4.4   Calculation of the **k**-space volume near the minimum of an acoustical branch.

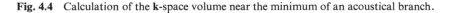

This behavior is quite different from the $(\omega - \omega_0)^{1/2}$ dependence which $\rho(\omega)$ exhibits at minima of optical branches or, for that matter, at nonabsolute minima which acoustical branches may have.

The constant in Eq. (4.55) can be evaluated in terms of the elastic properties of the solid. For this purpose we first compute the volume of **k**-space enclosed by a constant-frequency surface whose ω is small. Figure 4.4 shows that the element of volume included in a small solid angle $d\alpha$ is $\frac{1}{3}[\omega/c(\hat{\mathbf{k}})]^3 \, d\alpha$, so that the total volume is $4\pi\omega^2/3\bar{c}^3$; here $\bar{c}$ stands for a mean velocity of sound obtained by averaging the inverse cube of the actual phase velocity over angles. The total number of modes with frequency *up to* ω is therefore

$$\frac{V\omega^3}{6\pi^2\bar{c}^3} = \int_0^\omega \rho(\omega') \, d\omega'. \tag{4.56}$$

Differentiating both sides of (4.56) with respect to ω, we obtain

$$\rho(\omega) = \frac{V\omega^2}{2\pi^2\bar{c}^3}. \tag{4.57}$$

4.12   Specific Heat at Low Temperatures

It is clear that the integral (4.38) will have negligible contributions from those parts of the spectrum for which $\beta\hbar\omega \gg 1$. In particular, if we consider the limit of low temperatures (i.e., $\beta \to \infty$), we need only pay attention to the region around the minimum of the acoustical branches. Accordingly, we may substitute Eq. (4.57) into (4.38) obtaining[6]

$$U - U_0 = \frac{3V\hbar}{2\pi^2\bar{c}^3}\int_0^\infty \frac{\omega^3 \, d\omega}{e^{\beta\hbar\omega} - 1} = \frac{\pi^2(KT)^4 V}{10\hbar^3\bar{c}^3} . \qquad (4.58)$$

Equation (4.58) is analogous to the Stefan-Boltzmann law for electromagnetic black-body radiation. The latter differs, first of all, in the trivial respect that there are only two modes for a given $\mathbf{k}$, so that instead of $\bar{c}^3$ we should write $\frac{3}{2}c^3$, where c is the velocity of light. A more important difference is that the electromagnetic equation corresponding to (3.49) is *exact*, so that the Stefan-Boltzmann law remains valid at *all* temperatures, no matter how high.

In discussing low temperatures, a word should be added about the replacement of the sum over $\mathbf{k}$ by an integral. Such a step is justified if the number of modes with energy $\hbar\omega$ less than KT is very large. As a criterion we may, therefore, use the requirement that the lowest-frequency mode have an energy very small compared to KT; the frequency of this "fundamental" mode is of the order of the velocity of the waves divided by a linear dimension of the system. A simple calculation shows that for an electromagnetic cavity whose dimensions are of the order of centimeters deviations from the Stefan-Boltzmann law might be expected at a temperature of a few degrees Kelvin; but since typical sound velocities are smaller than the velocity of light by a factor of about 10^5, Eq. (4.58) holds for a solid sample of centimeter dimensions down to temperatures of a few microdegrees.

4.13   Interpolation

As the temperature increases, Eq. (4.58) fails; for obviously $\rho(\omega)$ deviates more and more from Eq. (4.57), vanishing altogether above the

---

[6] Equation (4.58) contains an extra factor of 3 to account for the presence of three acoustical branches. It is assumed, of course, that the averaging of c^{-3} in order to compute $\bar{c}$ is extended over branches as well as angles.

maximum frequency. We could, of course, modify Eq. (4.58) so as to put a finite upper limit on ω. If we call this limit $K\Theta/\hbar$, where Θ is some constant having the dimensions of temperature, we get

$$U - U_0 = \frac{3V}{2\pi^2} \frac{(KT)^4}{\hbar^3 \bar{c}^3} \int_0^{\Theta/T} \frac{x^3}{e^x - 1} \, dx. \qquad (4.59)$$

It is possible to choose Θ so that Eq. (4.59) is correct for the limit $T \to \infty$ as well (it is automatically correct for $T \to 0$). For when $T \gg \Theta$, x is always much smaller than 1, so that

$$\int_0^{\Theta/T} \frac{x^3}{e^x - 1} \, dx \cong \int_0^{\Theta/T} x^2 \, dx = \frac{1}{3}\left(\frac{\Theta}{T}\right)^3 \qquad (4.60)$$

and Eq. (4.59) becomes

$$U - U_0 = \frac{V}{2\pi^2} \frac{K^3 \Theta^3}{\hbar^3 \bar{c}^3} KT. \qquad (4.61)$$

Comparing (4.61) with (4.37), we see that the two agree provided we choose

$$K\Theta = \hbar\bar{c}\left(\frac{6\pi^2 \mathscr{R}\mathscr{N}}{V}\right)^{1/3}; \qquad (4.62)$$

the internal energy at arbitrary T then becomes

$$U - U_0 = 9\mathscr{R}\mathscr{N} KT\left(\frac{T}{\Theta}\right)^3 \int_0^{\Theta/T} \frac{x^3}{e^x - 1} \, dx. \qquad (4.63)$$

Equation (4.63) is Debye's formula. It is correct in the limits of high and low T, since that is what is was constructed to be; there is no particular reason to trust it at intermediate temperatures. On the other hand, it is clearly possible, by making Θ itself a function of T, to adjust (4.63) to fit experimental results. There is, moreover, a considerable practical advantage in reporting specific heat measurements by specifying Θ as a function of T, rather than directly: for whereas the specific heat easily varies over a few orders of magnitude (in fact vanishing as $T \to 0$), Θ remains relatively constant (generally well within a factor of two) for the whole temperature range.

PROBLEMS

1. Prove the two commutation rules (4.4).
2. Prove Eqs. (4.9) and (4.10).

3. Show that the addition to the Hamiltonian (3.28) of an "anharmonic term"

$$\frac{1}{6} \sum_{n_1 \alpha_1 i_1} \sum_{n_2 \alpha_2 i_2} \sum_{n_3 \alpha_3 i_3} \Lambda_{\alpha_1 i_1; \alpha_2 i_2; \alpha_3 i_3}(\mathbf{R}_{n_2} - \mathbf{R}_{n_1}, \mathbf{R}_{n_3} - \mathbf{R}_{n_1})$$
$$\times x_{i_1}(n_1; \alpha_1) x_{i_2}(n_2; \alpha_2) x_{i_3}(n_3; \alpha_3) \quad (4.64)$$

gives rise to matrix elements between states in which three phonon occupation numbers simultaneously change by unity. Show explicity that no matrix elements appear between states which do not have the same total crystal momentum. (Thus, for example, there will be matrix elements for a process in which a phonon $\mathbf{k}_1 \lambda_1$ is destroyed while two phonons $\mathbf{k}_2 \lambda_2$ and $\mathbf{k}_3 \lambda_3$ are created, but only if $\mathbf{k}_1 = \mathbf{k}_2 + \mathbf{k}_3$.)

4. Prove that, as $T \to 0$, the difference between Eqs. (4.58) and (4.59) vanishes faster than any finite power of T. Would you conclude that the difference between (4.58) and reality vanishes as rapidly?

5

Interaction with
Electromagnetic Radiation

5.1 Introduction

In this chapter we shall study the problem of two systems, namely the lattice vibrations and the electromagnetic radiation field, weakly coupled to each other.

We saw in Chapter 3 how the adiabatic approximation allows us to consider the vibrational motion of the lattice as a dynamical system separate from electronic excitations. The energy levels of this system are specified by the quantum numbers $N_\lambda(\mathbf{k})$, that is, by the occupation numbers of the various phonon modes; the radiation field similarly has energy levels specified by occupation numbers of *photon* modes. The fact that the particles constituting the lattice are electrically charged introduces a coupling which destroys the independence of the two systems, so that the quantum numbers can change with time and *transitions* occur. The last sentence can, in fact, be taken as defining the phrase "electrically charged."

Of course, the vibrational motion of the lattice is not the only motion of which a crystal is capable; in particular, *electronic* excitations also interact with the radiation field. From this point of view the present chapter comes prematurely, since we have not yet developed any formalism for such excitations. On the other hand, it is instructive to investigate just what kind of information *can* be obtained on the basis of such limited knowledge. We shall find that

(*a*) Certain exact *selection rules* can be derived for transitions between initial and final states which correspond to the same electronic state.[1]

---

[1] A "selection rule" is a statement to the effect that certain transitions are *forbidden*; it throws no light on how probable transitions which are *not* forbidden may be.

(*b*) Certain transition probabilities (or "intensities") can be calculated on the assumption that the electronic state does not change and that there is no electronic excitation resonant with the radiation.

Our first task is to provide a description of the *free* electromagnetic field in a convenient form. This will involve utilizing the geometrical periodicity of the lattice, even though its dynamical influence is at first neglected.

5.2 Free Radiation Field

Subjecting the free electromagnetic field to the same cyclic boundary conditions which apply to the crystal, we find that its normal modes are plane waves for which the vector potential **A** has the form

$$\mathbf{A(r)} = A_0 \hat{\boldsymbol{\epsilon}}(\tilde{\mathbf{K}}\lambda)e^{i\,\tilde{\mathbf{K}}\cdot\mathbf{r}-i\Omega t}. \tag{5.1}$$

Here $\hat{\boldsymbol{\epsilon}}(\tilde{\mathbf{K}}\lambda)$ is a unit polarization vector perpendicular to $\tilde{\mathbf{K}}$, and λ takes the two values 1, 2 to distinguish the two orthogonal polarizations for a given $\tilde{\mathbf{K}}$. The frequency Ω is given by

$$\Omega = |\tilde{\mathbf{K}}|\,c, \tag{5.2}$$

independent of λ; c is the velocity of light.

According to the theorems of Chapters 1 and 2, we can uniquely decompose the vectors **r** and $\tilde{\mathbf{K}}$ by writing

$$\mathbf{r} = \mathbf{R} + \boldsymbol{\rho} \tag{5.3}$$

$$\tilde{\mathbf{K}} = \mathbf{K} + \mathbf{k}, \tag{5.4}$$

where we require that (*a*) **R** and **K** be respectively vectors of the direct and reciprocal lattice, and (*b*) $\boldsymbol{\rho}$ and **k** lie within the respective proximity cells. Equations (5.1) and (5.2) then become

$$\mathbf{A} = A_0 \hat{\boldsymbol{\epsilon}}(\mathbf{Kk}\lambda)e^{i(\mathbf{K+k})\cdot\boldsymbol{\rho}}e^{i\mathbf{k}\cdot\mathbf{R}}e^{-i\Omega_{\mathbf{K}\lambda}(\mathbf{k})t}, \tag{5.5}$$

$$\Omega_{\mathbf{k}\lambda}(\mathbf{k}) = |\mathbf{K} + \mathbf{k}|\,c. \tag{5.6}$$

This change gives **A** the form of Eq. (2.11), as required by Theorem 1 of Chapter 2. The vector $\boldsymbol{\rho}$ takes the place of the parameter σ: each point in the primitive cell represents a degree of freedom for the electromagnetic field. The electromagnetic spectrum now has an infinity of branches, labeled **K**λ.

Consider as an example a simple cubic lattice of spacing a; the Cartesian components of the reciprocal lattice vectors are $2\pi L/a$, $2\pi M/a$, and $2\pi N/a$, with LMN integers. The frequencies of the various electromagnetic branches are then

$$\Omega_{LMN\lambda}(\mathbf{k}) = \frac{2\pi c}{a}\left[\left(L + \frac{k_x a}{2\pi}\right)^2 + \left(M + \frac{k_y a}{2\pi}\right)^2 + \left(N + \frac{k_z a}{2\pi}\right)^2\right]^{1/2}.$$

$$(5.7)$$

The first few are plotted in Fig. 5.1 as a function of k_x, with $k_y = k_z = 0$. Of course, the only change from Eq. (5.2) is one of labeling; we have merely "folded" the original $\tilde{\mathbf{K}}$-space into one Brillouin zone. The usefulness of such a scheme will become apparent in the following sections.

The quantization of the free field proceeds by a method analogous to the one we used for the phonon field in Chapter 4; we shall only quote the necessary results.[2] In the formulation of Eqs. (5.1) and (5.2) (that is, if the geometry of the lattice is not introduced), the Hamiltonian of the field becomes

$$H = \sum_{\tilde{\mathbf{K}}\lambda} [b_\lambda{}^\dagger(\tilde{\mathbf{K}})b_\lambda(\tilde{\mathbf{K}}) + \tfrac{1}{2}]\hbar\Omega_\lambda(\tilde{\mathbf{K}}), \qquad (5.8)$$

where the b's are creation and destruction operators for *photons* with properties identical to those of the a's of Chapter 4. The vector potential operator is given in terms of the b's by

$$\mathbf{A}(\mathbf{r}) = i \sum_{\tilde{\mathbf{K}}\lambda} \left[\frac{2\pi c^2 \hbar}{V\Omega_\lambda(\tilde{\mathbf{K}})}\right]^{1/2} [b_\lambda(\tilde{\mathbf{K}})e^{i\tilde{\mathbf{K}}\cdot\mathbf{r}} - b_\lambda{}^\dagger(\tilde{\mathbf{K}})e^{-i\tilde{\mathbf{K}}\cdot\mathbf{r}}]\hat{\boldsymbol{\epsilon}}(\tilde{\mathbf{K}}\lambda). \qquad (5.9)$$

If we now change our geometrical nomenclature to that of Eqs. (5.5) and (5.6), Eq. (5.8) is unchanged except for the system of labeling the modes:

$$H = \sum_{\mathbf{k}\mathbf{K}\lambda} [b_{\mathbf{K}\lambda}^\dagger(\mathbf{k})b_{\mathbf{K}\lambda}(\mathbf{k}) + \tfrac{1}{2}]\hbar\Omega_{\mathbf{K}\lambda}(\mathbf{k}); \qquad (5.10)$$

while Eq. (5.9) becomes

$$\mathbf{A}(\mathbf{R}, \boldsymbol{\rho}) = i \sum_{\mathbf{k}\mathbf{K}\lambda} \left[\frac{2\pi c^2 \hbar}{V\Omega_{\mathbf{K}\lambda}(\mathbf{k})}\right]^{1/2} [b_{\mathbf{K}\lambda}(\mathbf{k})e^{i(\mathbf{K}+\mathbf{k})\cdot\boldsymbol{\rho}}e^{i\mathbf{k}\cdot\mathbf{R}}$$
$$- b_{\mathbf{K}\lambda}^\dagger(\mathbf{k})e^{-i(\mathbf{K}+\mathbf{k})\cdot\boldsymbol{\rho}}e^{-i\mathbf{k}\cdot\mathbf{R}}]\hat{\boldsymbol{\epsilon}}(\mathbf{K}\mathbf{k}\lambda). \qquad (5.11)$$

---

[2] In order to quantize the electromagnetic field, it must first be described in terms of variables which can be treated as canonically conjugate coordinates and momenta. The problem is amply treated in standard texts.

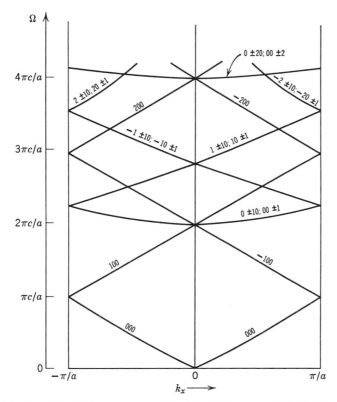

Fig. 5.1 Branches of the spectrum of the free electromagnetic field along the k_x-axis of a simple cubic lattice. The labels are the numbers LMN of Eq. (5.7).

5.3 Crystal Momentum of Photons and Selection Rules for X-Ray Scattering

It should be clear from the form of Eq. (5.11) that the same type of argument as was used for phonons can be applied to show that *the crystal momentum of a photon in mode* $\mathbf{kK}\lambda$ *is* $\hbar\mathbf{k}$. This fact allows some immediate conclusions about transitions which the presence of the crystal can induce in the electromagnetic field. Consider in particular *elastic photon scattering*, that is, the type of transition in which one photon disappears, another appears, and the crystal is left in its original state. Since total crystal momentum is conserved, the initial and final photon must have the same crystal momentum, so that $\mathbf{k}_i = \mathbf{k}_f$. Putting, as in Eq. (5.4),

$$\tilde{\mathbf{K}}_i = \mathbf{K}_i + \mathbf{k}_i, \qquad \tilde{\mathbf{K}}_f = \mathbf{K}_f + \mathbf{k}_f, \qquad (5.12)$$

we conclude that $\mathbf{Q}$, the difference between the initial and final propagation vectors as measured in free space, must be a reciprocal lattice vector.

In order for such a transition to occur, it is necessary to conserve energy as well; by Eq. (5.2) this means that $\tilde{\mathbf{K}}_i$ and $\tilde{\mathbf{K}}_f$ must have the same length. Such a criterion can always be satisfied by making $\mathbf{Q} = 0$, so that $\mathbf{K}_i = \mathbf{K}_f$. The process we are describing is then merely a change of polarization of the photon, which does indeed occur when electromagnetic

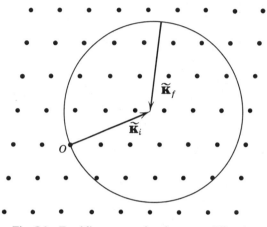

Fig. 5.2 Ewald's construction for x-ray diffraction.

waves propagate through a crystalline medium. If, on the other hand, $\mathbf{Q}$ is not to vanish, we must clearly have

$$2\,|\tilde{\mathbf{K}}| \geqslant |\mathbf{Q}|. \tag{5.13}$$

Since the shortest nonvanishing reciprocal lattice vector has a length of the order of $2\pi/d$, where d is the shortest interatomic spacing, it follows that the electromagnetic radiation must, to satisfy (5.13), have a wavelength of the order of, or less than, d. Thus, the fact that d is of the order of 10^{-8} cm limits this type of scattering to x-ray wavelengths or shorter.

The exact meaning of the selection rule we have derived is elucidated by a geometrical construction due to Ewald (Fig. 5.2). In the reciprocal lattice, place the vector $\tilde{\mathbf{K}}_i$ (propagation vector of incident monochromatic x-rays) with its tail at the origin, and describe a sphere which passes through the origin and whose center is at the head of $\tilde{\mathbf{K}}_i$. Now place the vector $\tilde{\mathbf{K}}_f$ so that its head is also at the center of the sphere; conservation of energy will then be satisfied if and only if the tail of $\tilde{\mathbf{K}}_f$ is on the surface of the sphere; whereas conservation of crystal momentum will be satisfied if and only if the tail of $\tilde{\mathbf{K}}_f$ coincides with a point of the reciprocal lattice. We conclude that diffraction of a monochromatic x-ray beam can only occur if its Ewald sphere goes through some reciprocal lattice points. Clearly, this criterion is not in general satisfied, so that an arbitrary monochromatic x-ray beam shows no diffraction. But note that:

1. If the x-rays are well collimated, but "white" (that is, they include a broad spectrum), this corresponds to a whole family of spheres of different radii; if the range of radii is large enough, some of these will satisfy the criterion for diffraction.

2. If the x-rays are monochromatic and collimated, and the crystal is rotated about some axis, this corresponds to fixing the Ewald sphere and rotating the reciprocal lattice. At each position where a reciprocal lattice point crosses the sphere the criterion for diffraction will be satisfied.

3. If the specimen is not a single crystal but a powder composed of small crystals in random orientations, there will be some angles through which monochromatic x-rays will be diffracted.

The above three cases correspond to the three methods commonly used in x-ray crystallography; they are called respectively the Laue method, the rotating-crystal method, and the powder method. In all cases one investigates the geometry of the reciprocal lattice using the Ewald sphere as a probe.

5.4 Photon-Phonon Interactions

It may seem somewhat surprising that the whole geometry of the reciprocal lattice can be obtained from x-ray scattering without saying anything about the form of the interaction or the composition of the crystal. The situation is rather analogous to the way in which equations for a diffraction grating can be obtained without knowing the shapes or widths of the grooves. Basically, this is possible only because we have assumed that the initial and final states of the crystal are the same. Note also that the information we have obtained is very limited: to calculate the *intensity* of scattered x-rays in various directions is not possible without knowing the details of the interaction; conversely, an experimental x-ray study of a crystal can yield much more information than just the geometry of the Bravais lattice.

In the present section we temporarily leave the further investigation of x-ray scattering and consider the coupling of the photon and phonon fields. We know from quantum mechanics that the interaction Hamiltonian is

$$H_I = \sum_{\alpha \mathbf{R}} \left[-\frac{e_\alpha}{M_\alpha c} \mathbf{A} \cdot \mathbf{p}(\mathbf{R}; \alpha) + \frac{e_\alpha^2}{2M_\alpha c^2} \mathbf{A}^2 \right]; \qquad (5.14)$$

here $\mathbf{p}(\mathbf{R}; \alpha)$ is the vector whose components are $p_1(\mathbf{R}; \alpha)$, $p_2(\mathbf{R}; \alpha)$, and $p_3(\mathbf{R}; \alpha)$, and $\mathbf{A}$ is the vector potential evaluated at the point where the atom $(\mathbf{R}; \alpha)$ is. The radius vector of this point is given by $\mathbf{R} + \boldsymbol{\rho}_\alpha + \mathbf{x}(\mathbf{R}; \alpha)$, where $\boldsymbol{\rho}_\alpha$ is the equilibrium position of the atom relative to the origin of the primitive cell.

Since the displacements $\mathbf{x}$ are presumed small, we can expand $\mathbf{A}$ in a Taylor series around the point $\mathbf{R} + \boldsymbol{\rho}_\alpha$. We indicate such an expansion schematically by

$$\mathbf{A} \sim \mathbf{A}(\mathbf{R}, \boldsymbol{\rho}_\alpha)(1 + \mathbf{x} + \mathbf{x}^2 + \cdots) \tag{5.15}$$

ignoring, for the moment, the magnitudes of the coefficients. In the same schematic form, the interaction Hamiltonian (5.14) will be

$$H_I \sim \mathbf{A}(1 + \mathbf{x} + \mathbf{x}^2 + \cdots)\mathbf{p} + \mathbf{A}^2(1 + \mathbf{x} + \mathbf{x}^2 + \cdots). \tag{5.16}$$

Now since $\mathbf{A}$ is, by Eq. (5.11), linear in the b's and $b^\dagger$'s, while $\mathbf{x}$ and $\mathbf{p}$ are

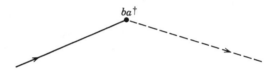

Fig. 5.3   Diagram for the conversion of a photon to a phonon.

linear in the a's and $a^\dagger$'s, the form of (5.16) in terms of phonon and photon operators is

$$H_I \sim (ba + ba^2 + ba^3 + \cdots) + (b^2 + b^2a + b^2a^2 + \cdots) \tag{5.17}$$

where each term represents, in addition to itself, corresponding terms with some or all operators daggered.

The point of putting H_I into such a form is that it allows us to read off the types of photon-phonon processes which are possible. Thus the term ba represents a one-photon, one-phonon process; for example, the destruction of a photon and simultaneous creation of a phonon. The term ba^2 might be the conversion of a photon into two phonons; or the "scattering" of a phonon from one state into another with the emission (or absorption) of a photon; and so on. The term b^2 gives rise to scattering of photons from one mode to another without change in phonon population—such as the elastic scattering of x-rays considered in the previous section; b^2a could be the inelastic scattering of photons with simultaneous creation (or destruction) of a phonon (as, for example, in the Raman effect).

It is extremely convenient to catalog these various processes with the aid of diagrams. If we let a photon be represented by a solid line and a phonon by a dashed line, then each term in the Hamiltonian represents a "vertex", i.e., a point where some lines begin or end. For example, the process of conversion of a photon to a phonon is denoted by an entering solid line, a departing dashed line, and a vertex labeled $ba^\dagger$ (Fig. 5.3). A number of other first-order processes are illustrated in Fig. 5.4.

Implicit in our use of these diagrams is the assumption that a process is dominated by the diagram with the fewest number of vertices, so that, for example, the matrix element calculated on the basis of Fig. 5.3 is not appreciably interfered with by a sequence of virtual states such as is shown in Fig. 5.5. The justification for this assumption is the same as for any other use of perturbation theory; if the perturbing Hamiltonian is small, then each vertex introduces into the matrix element an additional order of smallness. Nevertheless, as we shall see briefly in Sec. 5.7, it is possible for a higher-order process to be important if it is associated with a nearly resonant energy.

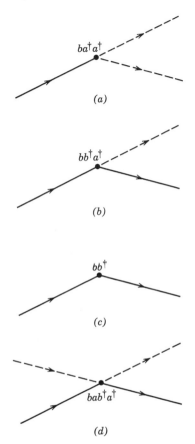

Fig. 5.4   The vertex in each diagram is marked with the term of the Hamiltonian which has the corresponding matrix element. (*a*) Conversion of photon to two phonons; (*b*) Raman effect; (*c*) photon scattering; (*d*) photon-phonon scattering.

5.5 Conversion of Photon to Phonon

In this section we shall calculate the probability of the process represented by the diagram in Fig. 5.3. For this purpose we need the interaction term represented schematically in Eq. (5.17) as ba, which means that only the $\mathbf{A} \cdot \mathbf{p}$ term in (5.14) is to be used and we are to evaluate $\mathbf{A}$ at the equilibrium position of the atom. In order to conserve energy, the frequencies of photon and phonon must be equal. As we noted earlier, photons belonging to branches with $\mathbf{K} \neq 0$ have frequencies in the x-ray range or higher, whereas the fastest lattice

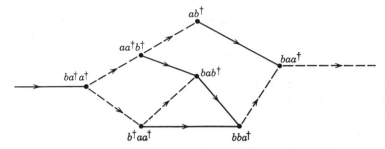

Fig. 5.5 A higher-order diagram having the same initial and final states as Fig. 5.3.

vibrations are of the order of 10^{12}–10^{13} sec^{-1}, corresponding to the optical infrared. Therefore, only the $\mathbf{K} = 0$ photon branch need be considered, and we can set $e^{i\mathbf{K} \cdot \mathbf{P}} = 1$ in Eq. (5.11).

Crystal momentum must also, of course, be conserved. This is not a requirement that needs to be separately imposed, for it follows automatically from the translational invariance of the interaction Hamiltonian. Explicitly, the b operator appears in Eq. (5.11) multiplied by $\exp i\mathbf{k} \cdot \mathbf{R}$, whereas the $a^{\dagger}$ in $\mathbf{p}$ carries with it a factor of $\exp(-i\mathbf{k} \cdot \mathbf{R})$ [cf. Eq. (4.9)]. Consequently, the result of the summation over $\mathbf{R}$ is to make all matrix elements zero for which the $\mathbf{k}$'s of photon and phonon are not equal.

Figure 5.6 is a superposition of the photon spectrum, Fig. 5.1, and of a typical phonon spectrum. Only a minute piece of the lowest electromagnetic branch can be seen on this scale; for the slope of the photon spectrum is the velocity of light, which is larger by a factor of about 10^5

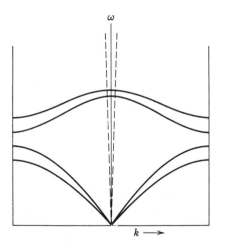

Fig. 5.6 Superposition of a typical phonon spectrum (solid lines) and the photon spectrum (dashed lines).

than a typical sound velocity. According to the previous two paragraphs, conversion of a photon to a phonon can only occur at points in this diagram where the spectra intersect. Accordingly, the only phonons which can be produced are optical phonons very near the center of the zone; their frequency determines the frequency of (infrared) radiation which the crystal will absorb. Incidentally, the diagram makes it clear that *in a crystal with but one atom per primitive cell, conversion of a single photon to a single phonon is impossible.*

Since the vectors $\boldsymbol{\rho}_\alpha$ are of the order of the lattice spacing, it is an excellent approximation for the present calculation to replace $e^{i\mathbf{k}\cdot\boldsymbol{\rho}_\alpha}$ in Eq. (5.11) by unity (this substitution is analogous to the dipole approximation in atomic physics). Thus finally the relevant part of the vector potential operator becomes

$$\mathbf{A}(\mathbf{R},\boldsymbol{\rho}) = i\sum_{\mathbf{k}\lambda}\left[\frac{2\pi c^2\hbar}{V\Omega_{0\lambda}(\mathbf{k})}\right]^{\frac{1}{2}}[b_{0\lambda}(\mathbf{k})e^{i\mathbf{k}\cdot\mathbf{R}} - b_{0\lambda}^\dagger(\mathbf{k})e^{-i\mathbf{k}\cdot\mathbf{R}}]\hat{\mathbf{e}}(0\mathbf{k}\lambda).$$

$$(5.18)$$

The interaction Hamiltonian can now be constructed by substituting (5.18) and (4.9) into the first term of (5.14). The term which will connect the state having one photon in mode $0\mathbf{k}\lambda$ to the state having one phonon in mode $\mathbf{k}\mu$ is the one containing the product of operators $b_{0\lambda}(\mathbf{k})a_\mu^\dagger(\mathbf{k})$, namely,

$$-i\sum_\alpha\frac{e_\alpha\mathcal{N}}{M_\alpha c}\left[\frac{2\pi c^2\hbar}{V\Omega_{0\lambda}(\mathbf{k})}\right]^{\frac{1}{2}}\left[\frac{M_\alpha\hbar\omega_\mu(\mathbf{k})}{2\mathcal{N}}\right]^{\frac{1}{2}}b_{0\lambda}(\mathbf{k})a_\mu^{\dagger}(\mathbf{k})\,\hat{\mathbf{e}}(0\mathbf{k}\lambda)\cdot\boldsymbol{\eta}^\mu(\mathbf{k};\alpha)^*.\quad(5.19)$$

Here $\boldsymbol{\eta}^\mu(\mathbf{k};\alpha)$ is the vector whose *i*th component is $\eta_i^\mu(\mathbf{k};\alpha)$. Since the matrix element of a creation or destruction operator between states of occupation number zero and one is unity, and the frequencies of phonon and photon are equal, the matrix element for the process we are considering becomes simply

$$\langle f|\,H\,|i\rangle = -i\sum_\alpha\hbar\left(\frac{\pi\mathcal{N}}{M_\alpha V}\right)^{\frac{1}{2}}e_\alpha\hat{\mathbf{e}}(0\mathbf{k}\lambda)\cdot\boldsymbol{\eta}^\mu(\mathbf{k};\alpha)^*.\qquad(5.20)$$

Defining a quantity $e_\mu(\mathbf{k})$ (sometimes called the "effective charge" of mode $\mathbf{k}\mu$) and a unit vector $\hat{\mathbf{n}}(\mathbf{k};\mu)$ by

$$\sum_\alpha e_\alpha M_\alpha^{-\frac{1}{2}}\boldsymbol{\eta}^\mu(\mathbf{k};\alpha)^* \equiv M^{-\frac{1}{2}}e_\mu(\mathbf{k})\,\hat{\mathbf{n}}(\mathbf{k};\mu),\qquad(5.21)$$

where M is the total mass of a primitive cell, we obtain

$$\langle f|\,H\,|i\rangle = -i\hbar\left(\frac{\pi\mathcal{N}}{MV}\right)^{\frac{1}{2}}e_\mu(\mathbf{k})\,\hat{\mathbf{e}}(0\mathbf{k}\lambda)\cdot\hat{\mathbf{n}}(\mathbf{k};\mu).\qquad(5.22)$$

Knowing the matrix element, we are in a position to calculate W, the transition probability per unit time, by the "Golden Rule"

$$W = \frac{2\pi}{\hbar} |\langle f| H |i\rangle|^2 \delta(E_f - E_i); \qquad (5.23)$$

the absorption coefficient $\varkappa$ for the infrared radiation is then given by

$$\varkappa = \frac{W}{c} = \frac{2\pi^2 \mathcal{N}}{VM} |e_\mu(\mathbf{k}) \,\hat{\boldsymbol{\epsilon}}(0\mathbf{k}\lambda) \cdot \hat{\mathbf{n}}(\mathbf{k}; \mu)|^2 \delta(\omega_{\text{phon}} - \Omega_{\text{phot}}). \quad (5.24)$$

Equation (5.24) exhibits a new selection rule: conversion of a photon to a phonon cannot occur if

$$e_\mu(\mathbf{k}) \,\hat{\mathbf{n}}(\mathbf{k}; \mu) = 0. \qquad (5.25)$$

If the crystal consists of identical atoms, it is clear from a comparison of Eqs. (5.21) and (3.51) that the process is, in fact, forbidden. Conversely, in an ionic crystal the infrared absorption is particularly strong, with $e_\mu(\mathbf{k})$ of the order of an electronic charge.

5.6   Width of the Infrared Absorption

The treatment of the preceding section predicts an absorption line which is infinitely sharp; such a result is characteristic of a transition between infinitely sharp energy levels. We can estimate the actual line width by calculating the lifetime of the optical phonon and using the uncertainty principle to attribute an energy width to it.

In a large perfect crystal, the process which limits the lifetime of the optical phonon is disintegration into two phonons through the anharmonic coupling which was discussed in Problem 3 of Chapter 4. Let us suppose, therefore, that we have an initial state which has one optical phonon of frequency ω_1 and momentum $\mathbf{k} = 0$, and we look for a final state containing two phonons of frequencies ω_2 and ω_3 and propagation vectors $\mathbf{k}_2$ and $\mathbf{k}_3 = -\mathbf{k}_2$. The matrix element due to the Hamiltonian (4.64) is easily found to be

$$\langle 2 \text{ and } 3| H |1\rangle = \Lambda \left(\frac{\hbar}{2M}\right)^{3/2} (\mathcal{N} \omega_1\omega_2\omega_3)^{-1/2}, \qquad (5.26)$$

where Λ is some average anharmonic constant and M is a typical atomic mass. The optical phonon disintegration rate R again follows from the Golden Rule (5.23):

$$R = \frac{\pi\Lambda^2\hbar^2}{4\mathcal{N} M^3\omega_1\omega_2\omega_3} \delta(\omega_2 + \omega_3 - \omega_1). \qquad (5.27)$$

When this rate is summed over possible final states the effect is that the δ-function is replaced by the density of final states. For simplicity we may assume that the final phonons are acoustic, with $\omega_3 = \omega_2 \sim |\mathbf{k}_2|\, c_s$, where c_s is the velocity of sound. Then ρ_E, the density in energy of two-phonon states of zero total momentum, is given by

$$\rho_E = \frac{9\omega_2^2 V}{8\pi^2 \hbar c_s^3}, \tag{5.28}$$

where three polarizations for each $\mathbf{k}$ have been assumed. If we also use the fact that $\omega_2 + \omega_3 = \omega_1$, we finally obtain

$$R = \frac{9\Lambda^2 \hbar V}{32\pi \omega_1 M^3 c_s^3 \mathcal{N}}. \tag{5.29}$$

The constant Λ can be roughly estimated by a consideration of macroscopic nonlinearity in the elastic properties of a solid. If the elastic potential energy is expanded in a power series in the strain (which is dimensionless), we would expect the coefficients to have comparable orders of magnitude; the reader may easily verify that the coefficient of the quadratic term is the elastic modulus, whereas the coefficient of the cubic term is essentially Λ. Hence, Λ may be expected to have the same order of magnitude as a typical elastic modulus.

In sodium chloride, for example, the infrared absorption band corresponds to $\omega_1 \approx 3 \times 10^{13}$ sec^{-1}. Inserting into Eq. (5.29) values of the various parameters appropriate to this crystal, we obtain $R \approx 10^{11}$ sec^{-1}, which would indicate a proportional half-width of $\frac{1}{300}$ for the absorption line. The observed width is about ten times larger than that, a result which can hardly be considered surprising in view of the fact that the value of Λ was estimated in such a crude way. The only sound approach is to consider the experimental line-width as a measurement of Λ; but for such a purpose the formula corresponding to Eq. (5.29) must, of course, be derived in much more careful detail. On the other hand, the quantity $\int \varkappa(\Omega_{\text{phot}})\, d\Omega_{\text{phot}}$, that is, the area under the absorption curve, is independent of line-width and is in fact in good agreement with experiment.

5.7   Intensity of X-Ray Diffraction

The selection rules for elastic x-ray scattering were worked out in Sec. 5.3; let us now investigate the intensities of the scattered rays. The discussion of Sec. 5.4 tells us that this process arises from the b^2 term in Eq. (5.17); that is, from the second term of (5.14) with $\mathbf{A}$ evaluated at the equilibrium positions of the atoms. Specifying now an initial state containing only a $\mathbf{kK}\lambda$ photon, and a final state with a $\mathbf{kK'}\lambda'$ photon instead, we obtain the matrix element

$$\langle \mathbf{kK'}\lambda' | \, H_I \, | \mathbf{kK}\lambda \rangle = \frac{2\pi\hbar\mathcal{N}}{\Omega V} \, \hat{\mathbf{\epsilon}} \cdot \hat{\mathbf{\epsilon}}' \sum_\alpha \frac{e_\alpha^2}{M_\alpha} \, e^{-i\mathbf{Q} \cdot \mathbf{\rho}_\alpha}, \qquad (5.30)$$

where $\mathbf{Q}$ was defined in connection with Eq. (5.12), $\hat{\mathbf{\epsilon}}$ and $\hat{\mathbf{\epsilon}}'$ are the initial and final polarization vectors, and we have set the two frequencies equal to each other since energy will have to be conserved. Equation (5.30) shows that the matrix element is proportional to the $\mathbf{Q}$th Fourier component of the quantity e^2/M.

The result (5.30) taken literally is quite incorrect, since it does not mention anything about the contribution of electrons to the scattering. The reason is that we have been tacitly holding on to the adiabatic approximation introduced at the beginning of Chapter 3. We claimed at that time that the electronic motion is rapid compared to that of the nuclei, which was true enough; it is not, however, fast compared to x-ray frequencies. A better interpretation of Eq. (5.30) would consist in including electrons as well as nuclei in the sum. Since electrons have a much lower mass, it is clear that they in fact dominate the mechanism, and that the intensity of the x-ray diffraction pattern gives the Fourier amplitudes of the electron charge distribution.

It may appear puzzling that Eq. (5.30) contains the mass of the scatterers in the denominator and is independent of their characteristic frequencies. Classically, we associate this type of inertia-limited polarization with the case of a driving frequency much higher than the characteristic frequency of the bound charges. Although this may be a good approximation for x-rays, it need not be so; we might expect strong modifications, for example, if the incident radiation were resonant with some electronic transition.

Since we have not yet developed any formalism for electrons, we can only give a qualitative discussion of this point. Typically, resonant scattering appears in a quantum-mechanical calculation as a second-order process in which a virtual intermediate state enters which almost conserves energy with the initial state. Figure 5.7 shows the diagram for such a process, in which a photon is converted to a virtual phonon, which is then in turn converted back to a photon. The effective matrix element for the process is

$$\frac{\langle \text{photon 2} | \, H_I \, | \text{phonon} \rangle \langle \text{phonon} | \, H_I \, | \text{photon 1} \rangle}{\hbar(\omega_{\text{phot}} - \omega_{\text{phon}})}, \qquad (5.31)$$

exhibiting the characteristic resonance denominator. Again, if we take this expression literally, it is of no particular interest, since x-ray frequencies are so much higher than phonon frequencies. On the other hand, it is clear that a diagram like Fig. 5.7, if interpreted as a virtual *electronic* excitation, could be associated with a very small energy denominator; this is precisely the case of a near-resonance that was mentioned earlier. In other words, the use of Eq. (5.30) to calculate electronic scattering of

Fig. 5.7 Second-order diagram for scattering of radiation. The contribution of such a diagram can be important if the energy is resonant.

x-rays (and we recall that electrons are the *dominant* scatterers) is justified only if we can *a priori* convince ourselves that the inertia-limited motion is the type which actually occurs.

PROBLEMS

1. The "cesium chloride structure" consists of two types of atoms, each type arranged on a simple cubic lattice in such a way that one type lies at the body centers of the other type. Compare the x-ray diffraction pattern from such a structure with the one which would be obtained if, without changing any positions, the two types of atoms were made identical, thereby changing the structure to body-centered cubic.

2. Birefringence is caused by the fact that there are matrix elements of the Hamiltonian which connect the state containing one photon to the state in which that photon is replaced by another having the same $\mathbf{K}k$ but different λ. Show that a single $bb^\dagger$ vertex can *not* give such a matrix element, but a second-order connection of the type shown in Fig. 5.7 can.

6

General Features of
Electronic Energy Levels

6.1 Introduction

There is only one correct way of approaching the study of the constitution of a solid, and that is to consider it as a many-body problem with as many constituents as there are particles in the actual piece of matter in question. The development of solid-state theory has been, since the advent of quantum mechanics, primarily a search for methods of approximation that would enable one to gain some insight into the behavior of the solutions to this basically unmanageable problem.

The adiabatic approximation, discussed at the beginning of Chapter 3, can again be used to advantage. First we note that in order to determine the electronic energy levels we may consider the nuclei fixed at their empirically known equilibrium positions. Second, we may be able to divide the atomic electrons into those belonging to closed shells, whose excitation potentials are high, and the relatively loosely bound valence electrons; the effect of the closed shells (the "core") upon the valence electrons will then consist only of a static potential.

When we come to treat the valence electrons, however, the problems become severe. We are faced here by a system comprising an immense number of particles (of the order of one valence electron per atom); the characteristic energies are all the same, while their mutual (Coulomb) interactions are by no means weak. We may consider four conceivable attacks on the problem:

1. Ignore the interaction between electrons. Such a procedure is absurd if we are after numerical results, but may be useful for qualitative insight.

2. Solve the problem with self-consistent fields; that is, consider each electron as moving in the average potential due to all the others. This is called the *Hartree method*.

3. Same as 2, but with the additional proviso that the wave function be not just a product, but an antisymmetrized product of one-electron functions. This is called the *Hartree-Fock method*.

4. Really solve the problem. This method, which has no special name, is in practice impossible.

It may be useful to introduce some nomenclature at this point which is often found in the literature. The difference in any quantity between what would be calculated by methods 4 and 3 is said to be *due to correlation*. Any difference between methods 3 and 2 is said to be *due to exchange*. Note that "correlation" and "exchange" are not physical phenomena, but names of mathematical patching procedures. If, say, the electron energy were correctly calculated (method 4), there would be no way of knowing which part if it is "exchange energy," or which part is "correlation energy," without also doing the *wrong* calculations 2 and 3.

In this chapter we shall approach the problem by method 1; that is, we shall investigate the motion of a single electron which is governed by a Hamiltonian

$$H = \frac{\mathbf{p}^2}{2m} + U(\mathbf{r}). \tag{6.1}$$

The results can, however, be interpreted as applying equally well to methods 2 and 3, since we do not specify what $U(\mathbf{r})$ is; it could be a Hartree or Hartree-Fock potential. On the other hand, we shall close our eyes completely to effects of correlation.

6.2   Bloch Functions

The outstanding characteristic of the potential $U(\mathbf{r})$ is its periodicity, which makes H commute with all the lattice translation operators. We may conclude immediately that a complete set of energy eigenfunctions can be found of the form (2.11):

$$\psi(\mathbf{r}) = \psi(\mathbf{R}, \boldsymbol{\rho}) = \chi(\boldsymbol{\rho})e^{i\mathbf{k} \cdot \mathbf{R}} \tag{6.3}$$

where $$\mathbf{r} = \mathbf{R} + \boldsymbol{\rho} \tag{6.4}$$

as in Eq. (5.3). Alternatively, if we let

$$u(\boldsymbol{\rho}) \equiv \chi(\boldsymbol{\rho})e^{-i\mathbf{k} \cdot \boldsymbol{\rho}}, \tag{6.5}$$

we obtain $$\psi(\mathbf{r}) = u(\boldsymbol{\rho})e^{i\mathbf{k} \cdot \mathbf{r}}. \tag{6.6}$$

Note that the exponential in the last expression is a continuous function of $\mathbf{r}$, so that $u(\boldsymbol{\rho})$ must be also. We may write $u(\mathbf{r})$ for $u(\boldsymbol{\rho})$ with the understanding that the values of $u(\mathbf{r})$ repeat periodically in each cell. Thus our wave function is a *plane wave modulated by a continuous periodic function*. This form is called a *Bloch function*.

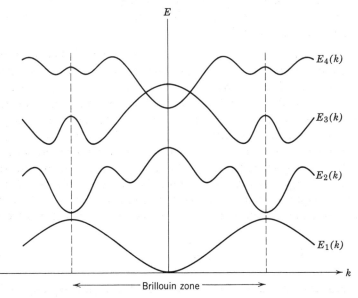

Fig. 6.1 Schematic one-dimensional picture of electronic energy levels as a function of k.

By substituting (6.6) into the eigenvalue equation $H\psi = E\psi$ written in position representation, we obtain

$$H(\mathbf{k})u(\mathbf{r}) \equiv \left\{ -\frac{\hbar^2}{2m} (\nabla + i\mathbf{k})^2 + U(\mathbf{r}) \right\} u(\mathbf{r}) = Eu(\mathbf{r}). \qquad (6.7)$$

This is a differential equation for u which is to be solved over a primitive cell subject to the boundary condition that the solution join smoothly to a repetition of the same function in the next cell. For a given value of $\mathbf{k}$, such a boundary condition will always give a discrete spectrum of eigenvalues which we shall denote by $E_n(\mathbf{k})$. The corresponding Bloch function will be written $\psi_{n\mathbf{k}}(\mathbf{r}) \equiv u_{n\mathbf{k}}(\mathbf{r})e^{i\mathbf{k}\cdot\mathbf{r}}$.

We know from the treatment of Chapter 2 that $\mathbf{k}$ may, without loss, be limited to the Brillouin zone. This fact also follows directly from Eq. (6.7). For let $u(\mathbf{r})$ be a solution of (6.7) with eigenvalue E; then the function

$$v(\mathbf{r}) \equiv u(\mathbf{r})e^{-i\mathbf{K}\cdot\mathbf{r}}, \qquad (6.8)$$

where **K** is a reciprocal lattice vector, will satisfy

$$\left\{ -\frac{\hbar^2}{2m} [\nabla + i(\mathbf{k} + \mathbf{K})]^2 + U(\mathbf{r}) \right\} v(\mathbf{r}) = Ev(\mathbf{r}) \qquad (6.9)$$

with the same eigenvalue. Since it also fulfills the boundary condition of cellular periodicity, we see that there is a one-to-one correspondence between the energies $E_n(\mathbf{k})$ and $E_n(\mathbf{k} + \mathbf{K})$. In other words, the functions $E_n(\mathbf{k})$ are periodic in the reciprocal lattice.

Figure 6.1 shows the situation schematically in a one-dimensional case. For a particular n, the function $E_n(\mathbf{k})$ sweeps out a quasi-continuous but finite range of energies referred to as an "energy band"; n is the "band index." Different bands may or may not overlap.

6.3   Average Momentum of Bloch States

The average momentum in a Bloch state is given by

$$\langle \mathbf{p} \rangle_{nk} = \int u^*_{nk}(\mathbf{r}) \, e^{-i\mathbf{k}\cdot\mathbf{r}} \frac{\hbar}{i} \nabla u_{nk}(\mathbf{r}) e^{i\mathbf{k}\cdot\mathbf{r}} \, d^3r$$

$$= \int u^*_{nk}(\boldsymbol{\rho}) \left(\frac{\hbar}{i} \nabla + \hbar\mathbf{k} \right) u_{nk}(\boldsymbol{\rho}) \, d^3\rho, \qquad (6.10)$$

where in the last step the domain of integration as well as the normalization of the u's has been switched to a primitive cell. Comparing with Eq. (6.7), we obtain

$$\langle \mathbf{p} \rangle_{nk} = \frac{m}{\hbar} \int u^*_{nk}(\boldsymbol{\rho})[\nabla_\mathbf{k} H(\mathbf{k})]u_{nk}(\boldsymbol{\rho}) \, d^3\rho, \qquad (6.11)$$

where $\nabla_\mathbf{k}$, the gradient with respect to **k**, acts on the operator $H(\mathbf{k})$ only.

To evaluate (6.11) we invoke the following theorem: given a Hermitian operator $\Omega(\alpha)$ depending on a parameter α, let $\varphi_\alpha(\mathbf{r})$ be a normalized eigenfunction of Ω and $\lambda(\alpha)$ its eigenvalue; then

$$\int \varphi^*_\alpha(\mathbf{r}) \frac{\partial \Omega(\alpha)}{\partial \alpha} \varphi_\alpha(\mathbf{r}) \, d^3r = \frac{\partial \lambda(\alpha)}{\partial \alpha} . \qquad (6.12)$$

Accordingly,

$$\langle \mathbf{p} \rangle_{nk} = \frac{m}{\hbar} \nabla_\mathbf{k} E_n(\mathbf{k}). \qquad (6.13)$$

The average *velocity* in a Bloch state is

$$\langle \mathbf{v} \rangle_{nk} \equiv \langle \mathbf{p}/m \rangle_{nk} = \nabla_\mathbf{k} \frac{E_n(\mathbf{k})}{\hbar} = \nabla_{\hbar\mathbf{k}} E_n(\mathbf{k}). \qquad (6.14)$$

The last two expressions are clearly equivalent, but they emphasize two different features. The first gives the velocity as the *gradient of frequency with respect to wave vector* and thus ties in with the familiar formula for the group velocity of a wave field. The second gives the velocity as the *partial derivative of the energy with respect to the corresponding component of crystal momentum* and is reminiscent of (half of) Hamilton's canonical equations. This latter analogy must be taken with a tablespoon of salt, since $\mathbf{r}$ and $\mathscr{P}$ are by no means canonically conjugate variables; a detailed discussion of their relationship will be encountered in Chapters 8 and 9.

6.4 Empty Lattice

As with the radiation field in Sec. 5.2, it is again instructive to examine the limiting case in which the lattice exists only in our geometrical imagination; that is, we set $U(\mathbf{r}) = 0$, which is, after all, a valid example of a periodic potential. Equation (6.7) becomes

$$-\frac{\hbar^2}{2m} (\nabla + i\mathbf{k})^2 u(\mathbf{r}) = Eu(\mathbf{r}). \tag{6.15}$$

The general solution is clearly a plane-wave exponential whose propagation vector must, because of the boundary conditions of cellular periodicity, be a vector of the reciprocal lattice which we call $\mathbf{K}$. The energy eigenvalue is then given, from (6.15), by

$$E_{\mathbf{K}}(\mathbf{k}) = \frac{\hbar^2}{2m} (\mathbf{K} + \mathbf{k})^2, \tag{6.16}$$

and the Bloch wave function becomes

$$\psi_{\mathbf{K}\mathbf{k}}(\mathbf{r}) = u_{\mathbf{K}\mathbf{k}}(\mathbf{r})e^{i\mathbf{k}\cdot\mathbf{r}} = e^{i\mathbf{K}\cdot\mathbf{r}}e^{i\mathbf{k}\cdot\mathbf{r}}; \tag{6.17}$$

note that $\mathbf{K}$ plays the role of the band index.

What we have obtained are simply the standard plane-wave solutions of the free particle, except that the usual propagation vector has been decomposed into a sum of a reciprocal-lattice vector and a vector lying in the Brillouin zone. Figure 6.2 is analogous to Fig. 5.1 for the radiation field; it shows the first few energy bands for a simple cubic lattice along the k_x-axis of the zone.

The bands of Fig. 6.2 do not look like those of our intuitive picture, Fig. 6.1. If we imagine replicas of Fig. 6.2 stacked next to each other, we find that it is indeed true that the *set* $E_n(\mathbf{k})$ is the same as the set $E_n(\mathbf{k} + \mathbf{K})$.

It would be stretching a point, however, to claim that the functions $E_n(\mathbf{k})$ are periodic, since a given band joins smoothly to a different band in the next zone; in other words, the curves giving the energy eigenvalues as a function of $\mathbf{k}$ cross each other. This behavior generally disappears as soon as a nonzero potential is introduced, as the next section will show.

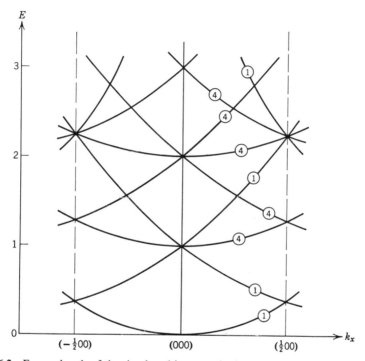

Fig. 6.2   Energy bands of the simple cubic empty lattice along the k_x-axis of the zone. Energy is in units of $4\pi^2\hbar^2/2ma^2$ and k_x in units of $2\pi/a$, where a is the direct lattice spacing. Bands are marked with the degree of degeneracy.

6.5   Weak-binding Approximation

Let us next consider the first-order effects of the potential viewed as a perturbation. We note first that, since U commutes with all lattice translations, it will have no matrix elements between states of different $\mathbf{k}$. For two states of the same $\mathbf{k}$, we find from Eq. (6.17) that

$$\langle \mathbf{K}_1\mathbf{k} \,|\, U \,|\, \mathbf{K}_2\mathbf{k} \rangle = \frac{1}{V}\int e^{i(\mathbf{K}_2-\mathbf{K}_1)\cdot\mathbf{r}}U(\mathbf{r})\,d^3r; \qquad (6.18)$$

in other words, the matrix element is independent of **k** and equal to the
$(\mathbf{K_1} - \mathbf{K_2})$-Fourier-component of the potential. In particular, the diagonal
matrix element is the same for all bands, being just the average value of
the potential. Clearly, we can set it equal to zero without any effect on
the energy level structure.

In the absence of diagonal matrix elements, the potential can have
first-order effects only if it connects two or more *degenerate* states, which
happens at points in the zone where two or more empty-lattice bands
cross. If only two bands are involved, the perturbed energies are given
by the eigenvalues of the matrix

$$\begin{pmatrix} E_1(\mathbf{k}) & \langle \mathbf{K_1k}|U|\mathbf{K_2k}\rangle \\ \langle \mathbf{K_2k}|U|\mathbf{K_1k}\rangle & E_2(\mathbf{k}) \end{pmatrix}, \qquad (6.19)$$

namely,

$$\tfrac{1}{2}[E_1(\mathbf{k}) + E_2(\mathbf{k})] \pm \{\tfrac{1}{4}[E_1(\mathbf{k}) - E_2(\mathbf{k})]^2 + |\langle \mathbf{K_1k}|U|\mathbf{K_2k}\rangle|^2\}^{\frac{1}{2}}. \quad (6.20)$$

Thus the bands cannot cross unless the matrix element vanishes,
which can sometimes happen if the lattice contains more than one atom
per cell. Consider, for example, a simple cubic lattice of spacing a, whose
basis consists of two *identical* atoms whose positions in the primitive cell
are $(0, 0, 0)$ and $\left(\frac{a}{4}, \frac{a}{4}, \frac{a}{4}\right)$. In other words, the crystal contains two
identical interpenetrating simple cubic lattices displaced by one-quarter of
a cube diagonal.[1] Denoting by U_A and U_B the potentials due to the two
lattices, we have

$$U(\mathbf{r}) = U_A(\mathbf{r}) + U_B(\mathbf{r}), \qquad (6.21)$$

$$U_B(\mathbf{r}) = U_A(\mathbf{r} + \mathbf{S}), \qquad (6.22)$$

where **S** is the vector $\left(\frac{a}{4}, \frac{a}{4}, \frac{a}{4}\right)$. The matrix element of U is then

$$\frac{1}{V}\int e^{i(\mathbf{K_2}-\mathbf{K_1})\cdot\mathbf{r}}(U_A + U_B)\, d^3r$$

$$= [1 + e^{-i(\mathbf{K_2}-\mathbf{K_1})\cdot\mathbf{S}}]\frac{1}{V}\int e^{i(\mathbf{K_2}-\mathbf{K_1})\cdot\mathbf{r}}U_A\, d^3r. \quad (6.23)$$

Letting $\qquad \mathbf{K_2} - \mathbf{K_1} = \frac{2\pi}{a}(L, M, N) \qquad (6.24)$

[1] This example does not represent a physically possible crystal structure, since its
basis has no symmetry element which is not also possessed by the rhombohedral lattice.
On the other hand, the same construction applied to the face-centered cubic lattice
would result in the *diamond structure*.

we see that the matrix element will vanish if $L + M + N = \pm 2, \pm 6, \pm 10$, etc. But even this cancellation is not exact, since the atoms in A and B have different near-neighbor configurations, so that their charge distribution will be distorted differently and U_A and U_B will differ by more than just a rigid translation.

Returning now to Fig. 6.2, let us examine the case of a higher degeneracy, namely, the four bands whose $\mathbf{K}$'s are (010), (0$\bar{1}$0), (001), and (00$\bar{1}$). Denote them by $|y\rangle$, $|\bar{y}\rangle$, $|z\rangle$, and $|\bar{z}\rangle$. Their unperturbed energies are:

$$
\begin{aligned}
E_y(\mathbf{k}) &= k_x^2 + (k_y + 1)^2 + k_z^2 \\
E_{\bar{y}}(\mathbf{k}) &= k_x^2 + (k_y - 1)^2 + k_z^2 \\
E_z(\mathbf{k}) &= k_x^2 + k_y^2 + (k_z + 1)^2 \\
E_{\bar{z}}(\mathbf{k}) &= k_x^2 + k_y^2 + (k_z - 1)^2,
\end{aligned}
\tag{6.25}
$$

where the components of $\mathbf{k}$ are in units of $2\pi/a$ and the energies in units of $4\pi^2\hbar^2/2ma^2$. For $k_y = k_z = 0$, all four bands are degenerate.

The weak-binding matrix elements which enter take a simple form if the origin is chosen at a point of symmetry T or higher, which is always possible in a cubic crystal. For brevity, we shall use the symbol U_{LMN} for the matrix element (6.18) with $\mathbf{K}_2 - \mathbf{K}_1$ given by (6.24). By using the four threefold axes of the point group T, it is then easy to show that

$$
\begin{aligned}
U_{020} &= U_{002} = U_{0\bar{2}0} = U_{00\bar{2}} \equiv A \\
U_{011} &= U_{0\bar{1}\bar{1}} = U_{0\bar{1}1} = U_{0\bar{1}\bar{1}} \equiv B.
\end{aligned}
\tag{6.26}
$$

Thus the Hamiltonian matrix for the four states is

$$
\begin{pmatrix}
E_y(\mathbf{k}) & A & B & B \\
A & E_{\bar{y}}(\mathbf{k}) & B & B \\
B & B & E_z(\mathbf{k}) & A \\
B & B & A & E_{\bar{z}}(\mathbf{k})
\end{pmatrix};
\tag{6.27}
$$

on the k_x-axis all four diagonal elements are equal and may be temporarily chosen as the zero of energy. The eigenstates of the matrix are then

$$
\begin{aligned}
|s\rangle &\equiv \tfrac{1}{2}[|y\rangle + |\bar{y}\rangle + |z\rangle + |\bar{z}\rangle], \\
|l\rangle &\equiv \tfrac{1}{2}[|y\rangle + |\bar{y}\rangle - |z\rangle - |\bar{z}\rangle], \\
|a1\rangle &\equiv \tfrac{1}{2}[|y\rangle - |\bar{y}\rangle + |z\rangle - |\bar{z}\rangle], \\
|a2\rangle &\equiv \tfrac{1}{2}[|y\rangle - |\bar{y}\rangle - |z\rangle + |\bar{z}\rangle],
\end{aligned}
\tag{6.28}
$$

and the eigenvalues are

$$E_s = A + 2B, \; E_l = A - 2B, \; E_{a1} = E_{a2} = -A. \qquad (6.29)$$

We note that the original quadruple degeneracy of the empty lattice has split into two singlets and a doublet. The calculation can, of course, be pursued further to obtain the four energies as **k** leaves the k_x-axis in various directions.

6.6 Symmetry and Degeneracy

We found in the previous section that after applying first-order perturbation theory some degeneracy remains on the k_x-axis of the Brillouin zone of a simple cubic crystal. Let us ask whether we can predict anything about the possible degeneracies that can exist after the problem is solved exactly.

The basic principle we shall use is: for every symmetry operation G which brings the crystal into itself, we can say that the state $G\psi$, where ψ is a stationary state of energy E, is itself a stationary state of energy E.

The symmetry operations which we have in mind are, of course, the ones which comprise the space group of the crystal. They can be classified, as we saw in Chapter 1, into translations, point operations, screw axes, and glide planes. It should further be clear that, since we have organized our states as Bloch waves, there is no further information to be obtained from the translational symmetry. A translation of the crystal will simply multiply each Bloch wave by a phase factor, clearly giving the same state.

Thus to study the degeneracy at a particular **k**, we need only pay attention to those operations of the space group which are not pure translations but which nevertheless leave the **k**-vector the same. This subgroup of the space group is called the *group of the wave vector*; it contains, in addition to the identity operation, only those rotations (including screws) whose axes are parallel to **k** and those reflections (including glides) whose planes are parallel to **k**.

An arbitrary **k** in the zone will, in general, have no rotation axes or reflection planes parallel to it, so that at a general (unsymmetrical) point there is never an essential degeneracy.

Suppose we now return to a symmetrical point in the zone (such as a point on the k_x-axis); let the group of the wave vector consist of the symmetry operations $G_1, G_2, \ldots, G_h$ (where G_1 is the identity operation).

Given a stationary state ψ_1, we then form

$$\psi_1 \equiv G_1\psi_1$$
$$\psi_2 \equiv G_2\psi_2$$
$$.$$
$$.$$ \hfill (6.30)
$$.$$
$$\psi_h \equiv G_h\psi_1.$$

We might at first sight conclude that the h states so obtained imply, if they are all distinct, an h-tuple degeneracy at this point, but such is not the case. Consider, for example, the state

$$\psi_s \equiv \psi_1 + \psi_2 + \cdots + \psi_h = (G_1 + G_2 + \cdots + G_h)\psi_1, \quad (6.31)$$

and form, for some j,

$$G_j\psi_s = (G_jG_1 + G_jG_2 + \cdots + G_jG_h)\psi_1. \quad (6.32)$$

It is easy to see that each of the products of two G's is itself one of the G's, and that in addition no two of the products are the same (the latter fact follows from the existence of a unique inverse for each operation). In other words,

$$G_jG_1 + G_jG_2 + \cdots + G_jG_h = G_1 + G_2 + \cdots + G_h, \quad (6.33)$$

the difference being only in the order of addition; and therefore, for all j,

$$G_j\psi_s = \psi_s. \quad (6.34)$$

Thus if we use, instead of $\psi_1, \ldots, \psi_h$, linear combinations of the ψ's of which ψ_s is one and all others of which are orthogonal to ψ_s, we find no symmetry reason why ψ_s should be degenerate with any of the others. In other words, the original h-tuple degeneracy was an accident of the particular Hamiltonian, rather than a consequence of symmetry.

We can now formulate the principle more generally: if linear combinations of the ψ's can be formed such that each one transforms into itself under all symmetry operations, then there is no degeneracy. The phrase "transforms into itself" does not, of course, preclude the appearance of a phase factor.

We shall now prove that if all the operations of the group of the wave vector commute with each other, then there is no degeneracy. For this purpose we first choose from the set $\psi_1 \cdots \psi_h$ as many functions as are linearly independent of each other and construct out of them an ortho-normal set. Let there be r functions in this new set, denoted by $\xi_1, \ldots, \xi_r$. Each ξ is a linear combination of ψ's, and each ψ is a (unique) linear combination of ξ's, from which it follows that the result of applying one of the G's to one of the ξ's will be to produce a linear combination of ξ's:

$$G_j \xi_t = \sum_{t'} g_j(tt') \xi_{t'}. \tag{6.35}$$

Furthermore, the nature of G as a rigid transformation of coordinates guarantees that if the set of ξ's is orthonormal, the set of $(G_j \xi)$'s will also be, so that the matrices $g_1(tt'), \ldots, g_h(tt')$ must be unitary.

It is clear that the matrix g corresponding to a product of two G's is just the matrix product of the two corresponding g's, so that if all the operations G commute, the matrices g must also commute. Now, it is well known that a set of mutually commuting unitary matrices can be simultaneously brought to diagonal form by appropriate choice of basis; in other words, it is possible to choose linear combinations of the ξ's such that each G_j merely multiplies each linear combination by some number, so that the condition of the previous paragraph is satisfied.

Returning now to the problem of the k_x-axis of a simple cubic lattice discussed in Sec. 6.5, the reader may easily convince himself that if, for example, the space group of the crystal is symmorphic and the class is T, T_d, T_h, or O, then the elements of the group of the wave vector all commute. Therefore, no degeneracy exists on the k_x-axis unless the crystal belongs to class O_h. But in the case of O_h degeneracy does exist, and the problem requires group theory for the treatment to have even a moderate amount of elegance.

6.7 Ordering of Bands

As we have seen, at an arbitrary, unsymmetrical point in the zone there is no degeneracy, so that the various bands can be simply numbered in order of increasing energy. We shall now prove the theorem that *any two unsymmetrical points in the interior of the zone can always be joined by a curve along which no degeneracy occurs.* The significance of this fact is that by virtue of it the numbering of bands in order of increasing energy at each nondegenerate point coincides with the analytic continuation of the functions $E_n(\mathbf{k})$, so that the bands are always "smooth." Of course, it is generally possible to find *some* connecting curves which *do* go through degenerate points; but that is immaterial, for at such points the functions $E_n(\mathbf{k})$ are not analytic anyway (since they are roots of a secular determinant).

Now for the proof. We have seen that degeneracies may in general occur when $\mathbf{k}$ is parallel to either a symmetry axis or a symmetry plane.

The loci of points in the zone for which the first condition holds form (straight) lines in the zone, and in connecting two arbitrary points by a curve such lines can always be avoided. The second condition is more serious, for the locus of **k**'s parallel to a symmetry plane is itself a *plane* through the origin of the zone. Thus we cannot generally avoid piercing this locus in connecting our two arbitrary points.

Suppose that a number of parallel glide planes Γ_1, Γ_2, ... exist in the crystal.[2] Let $\mathbf{h}_1$, $\mathbf{h}_2$, ... be vectors drawn perpendicular to the respective

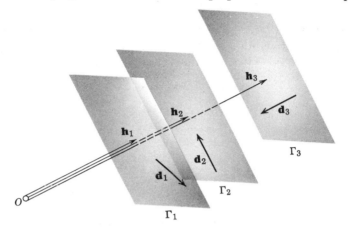

Fig. 6.3 Construction for the proof that there can be no planes of essential degeneracy in the interior of the zone: Γ_1, Γ_2, ... are parallel glide planes at $\mathbf{h}_1$, $\mathbf{h}_2$, ... which are characterized by glide displacements $\mathbf{d}_1$, $\mathbf{d}_2$ . . . .

planes from some arbitrarily chosen origin, as in Fig. 6.3; let $\mathbf{d}_1, \mathbf{d}_2, \ldots$ be the respective glide displacements. Then the operation Γ_i applied to an arbitrary vector **r** gives

$$\Gamma_i \mathbf{r} = 2\mathbf{h}_i + R\mathbf{r} + \mathbf{d}_i, \tag{6.36}$$

where R is the operation of reflecting a vector in a plane through the origin parallel to the Γ's. If now two Γ's are applied in succession, the result is

$$\Gamma_j \Gamma_i \mathbf{r} = 2\mathbf{h}_j + R(2\mathbf{h}_i + R\mathbf{r} + \mathbf{d}_i) + \mathbf{d}_j$$
$$= 2\mathbf{h}_j + 2R\mathbf{h}_i + \mathbf{r} + R\mathbf{d}_i + \mathbf{d}_j, \tag{6.37}$$

since $R^2 = 1$. Noting also that

$$R\mathbf{d}_i = \mathbf{d}_i, \tag{6.38}$$

$$R\mathbf{h}_i = -\mathbf{h}_i, \tag{6.39}$$

we get

$$\Gamma_j \Gamma_i \mathbf{r} = \mathbf{r} + 2\mathbf{h}_j - 2\mathbf{h}_i + \mathbf{d}_i + \mathbf{d}_j. \tag{6.40}$$

---

[2] An ordinary reflection plane can, of course, be viewed as a special case of a glide plane for which the glide displacement vanishes.

Thus the result of applying two Γ's in succession is a pure translation, so that the vector

$$\mathbf{R}_{ji} \equiv 2\mathbf{h}_j - 2\mathbf{h}_i + \mathbf{d}_i + \mathbf{d}_j \qquad (6.41)$$

must be a lattice translation vector (but note that $\mathbf{R}_{ji} \neq \mathbf{R}_{ij}$).

Consider now a Bloch wave function $\psi(\mathbf{r})$ whose $\mathbf{k}$-vector is parallel to the symmetry planes in question. Then

$$(\Gamma_j\Gamma_i - \Gamma_i\Gamma_j)\psi(\mathbf{r}) = \psi(\mathbf{r} + \mathbf{R}_{ji}) - \psi(\mathbf{r} + \mathbf{R}_{ij}). \qquad (6.42)$$

The difference between the two positions at which ψ is to be evaluated is thus a lattice translation vector, so that the periodic parts of ψ are the same at these two points. Moreover, this difference vector is given by

$$\mathbf{R}_{ij} - \mathbf{R}_{ji} = 4\mathbf{h}_i - 4\mathbf{h}_j, \qquad (6.43)$$

which is perpendicular to the planes; hence

$$\mathbf{k} \cdot (\mathbf{R}_{ij} - \mathbf{R}_{ji}) = 0 \qquad (6.44)$$

and the two ψ's are equal. We conclude that

$$[\Gamma_i, \Gamma_j]\psi = 0 \qquad (6.45)$$

for all ψ's in question, so that *all the elements of the group of the wave vector commute* and there is no degeneracy. In other words there are no surfaces of *essential* degeneracy in the interior of the zone. To complete the proof of the theorem stated in the first paragraph of this section, it remains only to show that surfaces of *accidental* degeneracy do not exist.

6.8 Accidental Degeneracies

There is a temptation to dismiss accidental degeneracies (i.e., degeneracies not due to some symmetry of the system) by the statement that they occur with vanishing probability, since the slightest refinement of the Hamiltonian will remove them. Such an argument may be considered sound in the case of, say, an atom, where the spectrum is truly discrete. In a crystal, however, the spectrum within a band is continuous and the degeneracy, in the ordinary sense of equality of energy eigenvalues, is huge. Of course, we have been using the word to mean the coincidence of two energies with the same $\mathbf{k}$. If now at some point in the zone two bands coincide, then a refinement of the Hamiltonian will in general *displace* the point of degeneracy rather than remove it. We may therefore in general expect that an arbitrary band structure does contain such points, the only "accidental" feature being their exact position. What we now propose to show is that such points form at most lines, but not surfaces, in the zone, so that the numbering of the bands is not thereby impaired.

Imagine the Hamiltonian matrix written in a Bloch-wave representation which approximately diagonalizes it in the sense that the off-diagonal elements are quite small compared to typical energy differences between bands. Then the diagonal elements can be considered good solutions for the functions $E_n(\mathbf{k})$ except at values of $\mathbf{k}$ where the differences among some $E_n(\mathbf{k})$'s are *atypically* small, that is, at or near a degeneracy point. Let $\mathbf{k}_0$ be a point where two bands, say $E_1(\mathbf{k})$ and $E_2(\mathbf{k})$, coincide. To find the behavior of the energies near $\mathbf{k}_0$, we need to diagonalize only a submatrix of H by writing the condition

$$\begin{vmatrix} H_{11}(\mathbf{k}) - E & H_{12}(\mathbf{k}) \\ H_{21}(\mathbf{k}) & H_{22}(\mathbf{k}) - E \end{vmatrix} = 0 \qquad (6.46)$$

whose solution is, as in Eq. (6.20),

$$E(\mathbf{k}) = \tfrac{1}{2}[H_{11}(\mathbf{k}) + H_{22}(\mathbf{k})] \pm \{\tfrac{1}{4}[H_{11}(\mathbf{k}) - H_{22}(\mathbf{k})]^2 + |H_{12}(\mathbf{k})|^2\}^{1/2}. \qquad (6.47)$$

The locus on which the two eigenvalues are equal is then determined by the *two* conditions

$$H_{11}(\mathbf{k}) = H_{22}(\mathbf{k}), \qquad (6.48)$$

$$H_{12}(\mathbf{k}) = 0. \qquad (6.49)$$

Each condition is an equation in the three quantities k_x, k_y, and k_z, that is, an equation of a surface in the zone. (It might appear that Eq. (6.49) is actually *two* conditions, since H_{12} is complex; but in fact H_{12} can always be made real by appropriate choice of phases of the basis.) Since the intersection of two surfaces is a curve, we see that *even to first order* no surfaces of accidental degeneracy can exist. When higher orders are considered, it may be found that even the curve shrinks to a single point; but for our purpose the limitation to a curve is sufficient in that the ordering of the bands by increasing energy is not impaired.

6.9   Time Reversal

The reality of the Hamiltonian implies that if $\psi(\mathbf{k})$ is an eigenfunction of energy with eigenvalue E, then $\psi^*(\mathbf{r})$ is also. Since the complex conjugate of a Bloch function of wave vector $\mathbf{k}$ is a Bloch function of wave vector $-\mathbf{k}$, we conclude that for each band $E_n(\mathbf{k})$ there exists a band $E_{n'}(\mathbf{k})$ such that $E_{n'}(\mathbf{k}) = E_n(-\mathbf{k})$. If we choose the convention of labeling the bands in order of increasing energy, a convention which the previous sections have shown to be consistent with analytic continuation, we conclude that *the functions $E_n(\mathbf{k})$ are even functions of* $\mathbf{k}$.

Thus time reversal introduces a symmetry into the band structure even if the crystal has no geometrical symmetry at all other than the translations. If other symmetries exist, they can often be coupled with time reversal to obtain new results.

Consider, for example, a crystal with a center of inversion. Starting with an energy eigenfunction $\psi_0(\mathbf{r}) = u_{nk}(\mathbf{r})e^{i\mathbf{k}\cdot\mathbf{r}}$, we may then reverse the sign of $\mathbf{r}$ to get a new eigenfunction $\psi_1(\mathbf{r}) = u_{nk}(-\mathbf{r})e^{-i\mathbf{k}\cdot\mathbf{r}}$. Applying time reversal to ψ_1 produces yet another eigenfunction $\psi_2(\mathbf{r}) = u^*_{nk}(-\mathbf{r})e^{i\mathbf{k}\cdot\mathbf{r}}$ which has not only the same energy, but also the same wave vector as the original ψ_0. If $\mathbf{k}$ is a general nondegenerate point, ψ_2 must be a multiple of ψ_0, from which we conclude that *at a nondegenerate point in a band of a crystal with a center of inversion, the periodic part of the Bloch function satisfies*

$$u^*_{nk}(-\mathbf{r}) = Cu_{nk}(\mathbf{r}), \tag{6.50}$$

where C is a constant of modulus unity. This constant can of course be adjusted to be 1, or -1, or any other preferred phase factor, by adjusting the phase of u_{nk}.

More complicated consequences of time reversal arise when we consider certain situations in which $\mathbf{k}$ is on a zone face. If a twofold axis perpendicular to a zone face exists, its combination with time reversal will take $\mathbf{k}$ to a point on the opposite face which is equivalent to the original one (that is, it differs from the original by a translation of the reciprocal lattice). The relationships can become so involved that the whole zone face becomes a *surface* of degeneracy; it is for this reason that the qualifying phrase "in the interior of the zone" was always used in our previous discussions of degeneracy.

PROBLEMS

1. Find the energies of the four states $|s\rangle$, $|l\rangle$, $|a1\rangle$, and $|a2\rangle$ of Eq. (6.28) when $\mathbf{k}$ is near, but not on, the k_x-axis. Neglect terms higher than quadratic in k_y and k_z.

2. If electron spin and spin-orbit interactions are to be considered, the Bloch functions must be written as two-component states

$$\psi_{nk} = \begin{pmatrix} u_{nk}(\mathbf{r}) \\ v_{nk}(\mathbf{r}) \end{pmatrix} e^{i\mathbf{k}\cdot\mathbf{r}}. \tag{6.51}$$

Show that the successive application of time reversal and space inversion changes ψ_{nk} into a state of the same $\mathbf{k}$ which is, however, orthogonal to the original one. It follows that in a crystal with a center of inversion every band is doubly degenerate even when spin-orbit coupling is taken into account. *Hint:* The time-reversed state corresponding to a two-component function $\begin{pmatrix} \phi \\ \chi \end{pmatrix}$ is $\begin{pmatrix} \chi^* \\ -\phi^* \end{pmatrix}$.

3. In Sec. 6.4 we set $U = 0$ and obtained Bloch functions whose periodic part u was independent of $\mathbf{k}$. Show that, conversely, the fact that $\nabla_\mathbf{k} u = 0$ implies that U is, at most, a constant. *Hint:* Prove that if $\nabla_\mathbf{k} u = 0$, then

$$[H(\mathbf{k}), \nabla_\mathbf{k} H(\mathbf{k})]u = 0.$$

4. The case in which $\chi(\rho)$, rather than $u(\rho)$, is independent of $\mathbf{k}$ is called the "tight-binding limit." Show that in that case E is independent of $\mathbf{k}$, so that the band has zero width.

7

Statistics

7.1 Introduction

If we were able to solve for the correct energy eigenstates of the crystal as a whole, we could state immediately that the probability of the system being in a state of energy E is proportional to $\exp(-E/kT)$, where k is the Boltzmann constant and T the temperature; at this point the present chapter would come to an end. But all we have is a more or less refined one-electron model, and the difficulty which is thereby introduced is best illustrated by looking at the case of an atom. If, for example, we solved for the *one-electron* states of mercury, we would find that the lowest energy level differs from the next higher one by many thousands of electron volts, so that it would appear that at ordinary temperatures all eighty electrons would certainly be in the lowest energy orbit.

The fallacy is, of course, that *there is no such state of the system.* There exists no wave function, not even an approximate one, which puts all electrons into the lowest orbit and at the same time satisfies the fundamental requirement that the function change sign under interchange of any two particles, as it must for particles of half-integral spin. The requirement of antisymmetry should be thought of as an intrinsic property of electrons, along with their charge, mass, and spin, and any "state" which violates it is absurd as a state in which the electron has a spin of three halves or zero mass.

The actual ground state of the mercury atom is denoted spectros-copically as $1s^2 2s^2 p^6 3s^2 p^6 d^{10} 4s^2 p^6 d^{10} f^{14} 5s^2 p^6 d^{10} 6s^2$. This symbol may be interpreted in two ways. First, it can mean an antisymmetrized product wave function which is an eigenstate of the Hamiltonian

$$H_0 = \sum_{i=1}^{80} \frac{p_i^2}{2m} - \sum_{i=1}^{80} \frac{80e^2}{r_i} \tag{7.1}$$

and which contains two electrons in $1s$-orbits, two in $2s$-orbits, six in $2p$-orbits, etc. Alternatively, it can stand for that eigenfunction of the Hamiltonian

$$H = H_0 + \lambda \sum_{i<j}^{80} \frac{e^2}{|\mathbf{r}_i - \mathbf{r}_j|}, \qquad (7.2)$$

with $\lambda = 1$, which *becomes* the wave function of the first interpretation if λ is changed adiabatically from 1 to 0. The second one is the actual wave function of the ground state of mercury. The first is not, but is nevertheless a wave function *which does exist*. On the other hand, $1s^{80}$ does not exist; for since there are only two linearly independent $1s$ orbits ("spin up" and "spin down"), no antisymmetric wave function can be constructed for more than two $1s$ electrons. Thus $1s^{80}$ stands for nothing in either interpretation.

The antisymmetry condition is often stated in the form of the *Pauli exclusion principle*, which says that no two electrons can have all their quantum numbers the same. It is important to realize that since electrons interact, there are no one-electron quantum numbers, and so it makes no sense to ask whether or not they are the same. The exclusion principle, taken literally, is meaningful only if the particles are sufficiently far apart for interaction to be negligible, and yet sufficiently close together for the available states to be "crowded." Physically, this is never the case. If the volume in which a given number of electrons is confined is made large, the density of available states increases, so that antisymmetric wave functions can be constructed for all but a negligible fraction of conceivable states of the system. If the volume is decreased so as to make anti-symmetry a significant requirement, the interaction energy invariably becomes significant as well. The literal Pauli principle can only be used to construct a complete set of states which, while approximate, are kinematically possible, so that they can then serve as a basis for solving the actual problem.

7.2   Fermi Distribution and Modifications

In this section we shall consider two kinds of electron states: "independent states" and "mutually exclusive states." An "independent state" is one which may be occupied by an electron or not and is unaffected by whether other electron states are occupied. A set of "mutually exclusive states" is a cluster of levels only one of which, at most, can be occupied by an electron.

Both types of states are idealizations. The independent state ignores interaction between electrons; we may hope that it will lose some of its absurdity by virtue of a Hartree calculation which does consider this interaction, if only in an average way. The set of mutually exclusive states represents, in a way, the opposite approximation, and is best explained by an example. A localized positive ion in the crystal will very often give rise to a spectrum of bound hydrogen-like electron states in its vicinity. If, however, one of these states is occupied, the field of the positive ion is shielded and the other states "disappear." In fact, of course, they do not disappear but shift into or near the continuum; but there the density of states is so high that one additional one makes no difference. The reader should note that a "single mutually exclusive state" is equivalent to an independent state.

Let a be an independent state of energy E_a; let $b_1, b_2, \ldots b_s$ be a set of mutually exclusive states of energies $E_b + \epsilon_1, E_b + \epsilon_2, \ldots, E_b + \epsilon_s$. Denote by $P(b_i)$ the probability that state b_i is occupied, and by $p(a)$ the probability that state a is occupied. Now compare the following two states of the total system:

1. State b_i occupied, state a empty, some particular filling of other states (of course the states b_j with $j \neq i$ must be empty);

2. All states $b_1, b_2, \ldots, b_s$ empty, state a occupied, all other states filled exactly as in (1).

The energy difference between (1) and (2) is

$$\Delta E = E_b + \epsilon_i - E_a, \tag{7.3}$$

while the ratio of the probabilities of state (1) and state (2) is

$$\frac{P(b_i)[1 - p(a)]}{\left[1 - \sum_{j=1}^{s} P(b_j)\right] p(a)}. \tag{7.4}$$

Since this ratio must be equal to the Boltzmann factor $e^{-\Delta E/kT}$, we obtain

$$\frac{1 - p(a)}{p(a)} e^{-E_a/kT} = \frac{1 - \sum P(b_j)}{P(b_i)} e^{-(E_b+\epsilon_i)/kT}. \tag{7.5}$$

Note that the left side is independent of the choice of b, while the right is independent of a; therefore, both sides must be equal to some number which is the same for all states. Since this number is positive by inspection, we can call it $\exp(-\zeta/kT)$, where ζ is a parameter having dimensions of energy. Upon solving for $p(a)$, we obtain

$$p(a) = \frac{1}{e^{(E_a-\zeta)/kT} + 1} \equiv f(E_a). \tag{7.6}$$

By equating the right-hand side of (7.5) to $\exp(-\zeta/kT)$, we further find

$$P(b_i) = [1 - \sum P(b_j)]e^{(\zeta - E_b - \epsilon_i)/kT}, \tag{7.7}$$

so that

$$\sum P(b_i) = [1 - \sum P(b_j)]ge^{(\zeta - E_b)/kT}, \tag{7.8}$$

where

$$g \equiv \sum_j e^{-\epsilon_j/kT}. \tag{7.9}$$

Therefore the probability of *some* state of the cluster b being occupied is given by

$$p(b) \equiv \sum P(b_j) = \frac{1}{g^{-1}e^{(E_b - \zeta)/kT} + 1}. \tag{7.10}$$

Ordinarily, E_b is taken as the energy of the lowest state of the cluster, so that all ϵ_j's are zero or positive. Then $g \to 1$ as $T \to 0$; at low temperatures the lowest state acts like an independent state, while the probability of other states of the cluster being occupied becomes vanishingly small.

The single parameter ζ, called the Fermi energy, determines all occupation probabilities of states which are either independent or mutually exclusive. The formula (7.6) is, of course, the celebrated Fermi-Dirac distribution. Note that it applies only to independent energy levels, which themselves represent a rather crude model of reality, and it does not compare in fundamental significance to the Boltzmann distribution from which it was derived.

7.3   Holes

For an independent state, only two situations are possible: either it is occupied by one electron, or it is not occupied at all. We may say equivalently that it is either occupied by an electron, or "occupied by a hole." The probability of being occupied by a hole is

$$1 - f(E) = \frac{1}{e^{(\zeta - E)/kT} + 1}. \tag{7.11}$$

Thus the Fermi function gives the correct distribution for holes as well, provided the direction of the energy scale is reversed.

The definition of a hole, as here given, suffers from all the crudeness of the independent-electron approximation. In fact, however, there are cases when the validity of this concept is much greater. Consider first the case where electrons do not interact, so that *all* states are independent, and let a particular band contain one electron less than is necessary to fill it completely; in other words, *let the band contain one hole.* If now the electron-electron interaction is turned on, it will mix into this state various excited states in which electrons are raised from the almost full band to empty states in higher bands. The modification of energy which consequently occurs is by no means small, since the electron-electron interaction is by no means weak.

If we now return to noninteracting electrons and consider the case of a band containing two holes, we would write for the energy[1] of the band

$$E_0(\mathbf{k}_1, \mathbf{k}_2) = E_0(\mathbf{k}_1) + E_0(\mathbf{k}_2), \tag{7.12}$$

where $\mathbf{k}_1$ and $\mathbf{k}_2$ are the crystal momenta of the two holes, and $E_0(\mathbf{k})$ is the one-hole energy function.[2] We may now inquire what would happen to Eq. (7.12) as a result of the electron-electron interaction. If we denote by $E(\mathbf{k})$ the one-hole energy function with interaction, then the modified energy of the state $(\mathbf{k}_1, \mathbf{k}_2)$ becomes

$$E(\mathbf{k}_1, \mathbf{k}_2) = E(\mathbf{k}_1) + E(\mathbf{k}_2) + \text{corrections}. \tag{7.13}$$

The origin of the "corrections" is the difference between the virtual excitations of which the one- and two-hole states are capable; for example, the one-hole state $\mathbf{k}_1$ can mix with a state in which the electron at $-\mathbf{k}_2$ is excited to a higher band, whereas the two-hole state $(\mathbf{k}_1, \mathbf{k}_2)$ does not have an electron at $-\mathbf{k}_2$ and is therefore incapable of such an excitation. We would, however, expect the total of such correction to be negligible as long as the number of holes is negligible compared to the number of excitable electrons.

Extending the argument to more than two holes, and taking into account that the Coulomb matrix element between electrons peaks strongly at small momentum differences, we come to the following conclusion: the independent-hole picture is valid provided that, in the region of the Brillouin zone where the hole is, the density of holes is small compared to the density of states. Quite analogously, the independent-electron picture is valid provided the surrounding density of *electrons* is small compared to the density of states.

Comparing the last statement with Eqs. (7.6) and (7.11), we see that electrons exist well above the Fermi energy, whereas holes exist well

---

[1] An arbitrary constant can, of course, be added to either side of Eq. (7.12), since there is no meaningful way of comparing absolutely the energy of one hole with the energy of two. The actual meaning of the equation is that, except for an additive constant, the variations of both sides with $\mathbf{k}_1$ and $\mathbf{k}_2$ are the same.

[2] The crystal momentum of a hole is taken to be the negative of the crystal momentum of the missing electron.

below the Fermi energy. Right near the Fermi energy neither particle is well defined, and there exists the possibility of strongly correlated states such as arise, for example, in the theory of superconductivity.

7.4 Density of States and Specific Heat of Electrons

On the basis of an independent-particle model, the number of electrons occupying states whose energies lie in an interval dE around the value E is $N(E)f(E)\,dE$, where $N(E)$ is the "density of states," that is, the number of states which exist per unit energy interval around E. This density is given by an expression analogous to the one derived for the frequency distribution of phonons, Eq. (4.41):

$$N(E) = \frac{V}{\hbar(2\pi)^3} \int \frac{dS}{|\mathbf{v}|}, \qquad (7.14)$$

where the integral is over a constant-energy surface in the Brillouin zone, and $\mathbf{v}$ is the average velocity given by Eq. (6.14). Here, too, critical points must exist, but they are not generally of great practical importance. The reason is that, for most processes, the only states that matter are those which are *not* all empty or all full, i.e., those which are within a few times kT of the Fermi energy. Since kT is small compared to a typical width of a band, it is not likely that a critical point will occur in this range.

It is easy to estimate the specific heat of electrons on the independent-state picture. At $T = 0$ all states up to the Fermi energy ζ are occupied, whereas all the higher states are empty. At a finite temperature there will be an appreciable population of electrons up to about kT above ζ, and an appreciable population of holes down to about kT below ζ. Therefore, there will be a total of about $N(\zeta)kT$ electrons and holes, all with energy about kT relative to ζ, giving a total energy content (relative to $T = 0$) of the order of $N(\zeta)(kT)^2$. An accurate calculation actually gives $(\pi^2/6)N(\zeta)(kT)^2$; the important fact is that the energy is proportional to T^2, giving a specific heat proportional to T.

7.5 Width of Bands

The *valence band*, that is, the highest band which is filled to an appreciable extent, must have a width of the same order as the spacing of atomic energy levels, or a few electron-volts. The argument runs as follows. Suppose we imagine the atoms of the crystal arranged on a lattice which is geometrically similar to the actual one, but of much larger spacing, so that interaction *between* atoms is negligible. The energy levels of this "crystal" are simply the sharp levels of the atoms. Of course, formally speaking, all the discussion of Chapter 6 is still applicable, but the "bands" have zero width. If we now begin to decrease the spacing, the energy of the system must decrease, for if there were no attractive forces between atoms, the actual crystal would not correspond to a physically real one. For large a, where a is the spacing, the energy would typically go as some negative power of a.

Yet somewhere this attraction must cease, since the physical crystal does not in fact shrink to a point. In other words, at some value of a the functional dependence of energy on a must change. This can happen only if some approximation which is applicable to the calculation of energy at large a breaks down badly; in particular, when at least some of the atomic orbits begin to overlap. Thus the perturbation of energy of the largest filled orbits, that is, those of highest energy, must be appreciable in the actual physical crystal, where "appreciable" means comparable with typical atomic energies; but it is precisly these levels which turn into the highest filled band.

We have seen that the electronic specific heat of a metal is determined by the density of states at the Fermi energy. For a reasonably well-behaved band, this quantity is of the order of the number of atoms divided by the width of the band. This argument yields, as an estimate of the specific heat per atom,

$$\text{spec. heat} \approx k(kT/\text{a few e.v.}). \tag{7.15}$$

There are two ways in which the electronic specific heat can be considerably smaller than Eq. (7.15): the valence band may be almost full; or it may be completely full, with the electrons overflowing to a small extent into the next higher band. In either case, the density of states at the Fermi level is much smaller than it would be near the middle of a band; substances for which such a situation obtains are often called *semimetals*. In the extreme case of insulators, the valence band is completely full and the next-higher band completely empty. The Fermi energy then falls in a forbidden gap and the electronic specific heat vanishes altogether.

A special situation occurs in the transition metals. The atoms of these elements are characterized by $4s$ and $3d$ states which are very close together in energy, even though the $4s$-orbits are much larger. The resulting crystal may be qualitatively described as having an "s-band" and "d-band" which overlap. The s-band has a "normal" width, i.e., a few electron volts; the d-band is much narrower, since the d-orbits of neighboring atoms hardly touch. Figure 7.1 shows the resulting density

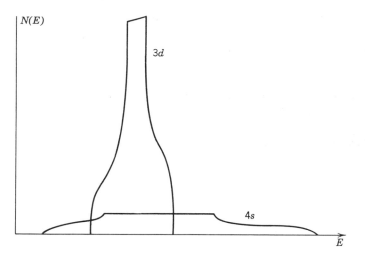

Fig. 7.1 Schematic representation of the density of states due to overlapping *s* and *d* bands.

of states; it is clear that if the Fermi energy is near the middle of the *d*-band, the specific heat can be much larger than the general estimate of Eq. (7.15).

7.6 Semiconductors

In the last section we described an *insulator* as a crystal for which the Fermi energy falls within a forbidden gap; the same criterion applies to *semiconductors* as well. The distinction is that when we describe a crystal as a semiconductor, we are implying that even though none of its bands deviate very much from being either completely full or completely empty, it is precisely this deviation which for one reason or another interests us. We may however, for most purposes, take it for granted that no band higher than the first one above the Fermi energy contains any electrons, nor does any band lower than the first one below the Fermi energy contain any holes. The latter band, of course, is the valence band; the former is called the "conduction band."

The number of electrons in the conduction band is, per unit volume,

$$n = \int N_c(E) f(E)\, dE, \qquad (7.16)$$

where $N_c(E)$ is the density of states in the band divided by the crystal volume, and $f(E)$ the Fermi function. For the case of semiconductors, two simplifications may be made in this integral. First, since all conduction band energies are many times kT above the Fermi level, the Fermi function may be approximated by

$$f(E) \approx e^{-(E-\zeta)/kT}. \tag{7.17}$$

Second, of the electrons in the conduction band, an overwhelming fraction will be found within a few times kT of the band minimum. We may therefore, by using the arguments about critical points from Chapter 4, replace $N_c(E)$ by $K(E - E_c)^{\frac{1}{2}}$ and let the upper limit go to infinity. The integral then becomes

$$n = e^{(\zeta-E_c)/kT} \int_0^\infty K\epsilon^{\frac{1}{2}} e^{-\epsilon/kT} \, d\epsilon, \tag{7.18}$$

where $\epsilon \equiv E - E_c$ is the energy measured from the lower edge of the conduction band. Evaluating the integral, we find

$$n = N_c e^{(\zeta-E_c)/kT}, \tag{7.19}$$

where
$$N_c \equiv \frac{K\sqrt{\pi}\,(kT)^{\frac{3}{2}}}{2} \equiv 2\left(\frac{2\pi m_c^* kT}{\hbar^2}\right)^{\frac{3}{2}}. \tag{7.20}$$

The last equation defines the quantity m_c^*, which is called[3] the "density-of-states effective mass of electrons." The number of electrons n is determined as though the whole band consisted of N_c states all at energy E_c. Although N_c is a function of temperature, it varies slowly compared to the exponential which accompanies it; nevertheless, we would not be justified in assuming that n varies rapidly with temperature, since as yet nothing has been said about the variation of ζ.

Because a reversal of the energy scale changes the Fermi function into an identical distribution function for holes, the number of holes in the valence band per unit volume can be calculated in an exactly analogous way. Calling the number p, we find

$$p = N_v e^{(E_v-\zeta)/kT} \tag{7.21}$$

$$N_v \equiv 2\left(\frac{2\pi m_v^* kT}{\hbar^2}\right)^{\frac{3}{2}}. \tag{7.22}$$

By combining Eqs. (7.19) anc (7.21), the important result

$$np = N_c N_v e^{-E_G/kT} \equiv n_i^2, \tag{7.23}$$

[3] For free electrons subjected to periodic boundary conditions, the density of states has the form $KE^{\frac{1}{2}}$, where K is given by Eq. (7.20) if m_c^* is replaced by the ordinary free-electron mass.

where E_G is the width of the forbidden gap, is obtained. This last equation does not contain ζ, and therefore allows an immediate conclusion: except for the slow variation of $N_c N_v$, the product of electron and hole densities varies exponentially with temperatures according to an "activation law" whose "activation energy " is E_G.

7.7   Calculation of Electron and Hole Densities

The next step is to determine the position of the Fermi level, and hence the values of the quantities n and p separately. To do this we impose the condition that the crystal must be electrically neutral. There is nothing, of course, to preclude a semiconductor being rubbed with a piece of cat's fur and thus acquiring a static charge; but such a charge would reside entirely on its surface and would not affect the electron and hole populations in the interior.

Accordingly, the total number of electrons per unit volume must remain constant as the temperature is varied, since the nuclear charge does not change; when translated into conduction band electrons and valence band holes, the statement becomes

$$N_0 \equiv n - p = \text{constant}. \tag{7.24}$$

Combining this constraint with Eq. (7.23) and solving for n and p, we obtain

$$n = \frac{N_0}{2} + \left(\frac{N_0^2}{4} + n_i^2\right)^{1/2} \tag{7.25}$$

$$p = -\frac{N_0}{2} + \left(\frac{N_0^2}{4} + n_i^2\right)^{1/2}. \tag{7.26}$$

We shall see in the next section how N_0 is determined.

Meanwhile, it is convenient to introduce the following terminology: a semiconductor crystal is called *n-type* if $N_0 > 0$, *p-type* if $N_0 < 0$; also it is called *intrinsic* if $n_i \gg |N_0|$, *extrinsic* if $n_i \ll |N_0|$. The second distinction depends on temperature, for we have seen n_i to increase sharply with T; all semiconductors become intrinsic at high enough temperatures.

For the intrinsic case, Eqs. (7.25) and (7.26) give

$$n \approx p \approx n_i, \tag{7.27}$$

independent of N_0. On the other hand, the extrinsic densities are:

n-type: $n \approx N_0$, $p \approx n_i^2/N_0$, $n \gg p$;

p-type: $n \approx n_i^2/|N_0|$, $p \approx |N_0|$, $p \gg n$.

7.8   Donors and Acceptors

The number N_0 is the charge density in units of $|e|$ which the crystal has when $n = p = 0$, that is, when the valence band is completely full and the conduction band is completely empty. In a chemically pure semiconductor this number vanishes; but in the presence of certain types of impurities it takes on a finite value. Consider, for example, a covalent semiconductor such as germanium. Its crystal structure is of the diamond type, in which each atom shares its four valence electrons with its four nearest neighbors. A tetravalent impurity, such as silicon, can easily be accommodated substitutionally without upsetting the charge balance. On the other hand, a pentavalent impurity, such as phosphorus, antimony, or arsenic, does not fit the lattice in its neutral state, but does in its singly ionized state: P^+, Sb^+, and As^+ all have four valence electrons available. Therefore, if one of these impurities is substituted for some germanium atoms, N_0 will take on a positive value equal to the density of impurity atoms. An impurity which causes N_0 to be greater than zero is called a *donor*.

In analogous fashion, a trivalent impurity, such as aluminum, indium, or gallium will, if it enters the germanium lattice substitutionally, appear as a negatively charged ion, causing N_0 to be negative. Such an impurity is called an *acceptor*. In general, if there are N_D donors and N_A acceptors per unit volume, N_0 will be given by

$$N_0 = N_D - N_A, \tag{7.28}$$

assuming all donors and acceptors to be singly charged. If some of them are multiply charged, Eq. (7.28) must be modified in an obvious way.

We have made the assumption that the presence of donors and acceptors alters the density of electrons but does nothing to disturb their energy-level structure. Such is not actually the case. We shall see in Chapter 9 that the presence of charged impurities gives rise to localized electron and hole states within the forbidden gap; a typical situation is shown in Fig. 7.2. Ordinarily, the number of states in the conduction band is so much greater than the number of donor states that if kT is comparable to ϵ_D or greater the occupation of the donor states is negligible. A similar argument holds for holes, and as a result our previous calculations for n and p should be good except at very low temperatures.

Suppose, however, that kT becomes small compared to ϵ_D and ϵ_A. Let n and p, as before, represent the density of particles in their respective bands; let n_D and p_A represent the densities of bound electrons and holes.

Equation (7.24) is then replaced by

$$n + n_D - p - p_A = N_0 \equiv N_D - N_A. \tag{7.29}$$

If we imagine the Fermi energy to be somewhere well in the interior of the gap, removed by many times kT from all energy levels, then the whole left member of Eq. (7.29) would vanish; clearly this cannot be the case unless N_D and N_A are exactly equal. We may, however, assume that *either p* and p_A, *or n* and n_D, are negligible, since the Fermi energy certainly cannot

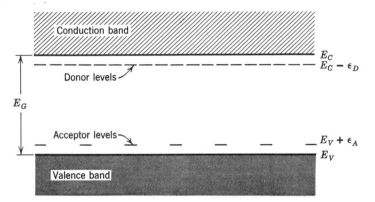

Fig. 7.2 Energy levels relevant to semiconductor statistics. The "abscissa" in this diagram represents position in the crystal, and the dashes are energy levels whose wave functions are localized.

be near the electron levels and the hole levels at the same time. Taking the first choice, we obtain[4]

$$n = N_c e^{(\zeta - E_c)/kT} \tag{7.30}$$

$$n_D = \frac{N_D}{e^{(E_D - \zeta)/kT} + 1} \tag{7.31}$$

$$n + n_D = N_0. \tag{7.32}$$

Eliminating ζ and n_D yields the quadratic equation for n

$$n^2 + (N_A + N_c e^{-\epsilon_D/kT})n - N_0 N_c e^{-\epsilon_D/kT} = 0. \tag{7.33}$$

At very low temperatures, the coefficient of the linear term approaches the constant value N_A, whereas the third term of the equation approaches zero.

[4] Equation (7.31) should contain the factor g^{-1}, as in Eq. (7.10). We omit it, however since its evaluation depends on the detailed structure of the donor level, and since it does not affect the general behavior which interests us.

Therefore, n approaches zero, so that n^2 may be neglected, with the result

$$n = \frac{N_0 N_c}{N_A} e^{-\epsilon_D/kT}. \tag{7.34}$$

On the other hand, at high temperatures N_c dominates the linear coefficient, since $N_c \gg N_A$. The quadratic term is again negligible, so that the equation becomes

$$n = N_0, \tag{7.35}$$

in agreement with the result of Sec. 7.7.

For a p-type crystal, in which $N_0 < 0$, Eq. (7.34) makes no sense; in this case we must neglect n and n_D compared to p and p_A. The results are completely analogous to Eqs. (7.34) and (7.35) and can be obtained by making the obvious substitutions.

PROBLEMS

1. (a) Show that in a semiconductor with $N_D > N_A > 0$, the Fermi energy in the limit $T \to 0$ approaches the energy of the donor levels.
   (b) Show that in a semiconductor with $N_D > N_A = 0$, the Fermi energy in the limit $T \to 0$ approaches a value halfway between the donor levels and the conduction band edge.
   (c) Since no semiconductor can in practice have N_A *exactly* zero, what is the physical meaning of (b)?

2. The "bound hole states" around an acceptor ion represent various ways of *removing* an electron from the vicinity. Let $c_1, c_2, \ldots, c_s$ represent a cluster of electron states *at most one of which can be empty;* find the probability that one of them is, in fact, empty. (This formula is the hole analogy to Eq. 7.10.)

3. Prove the statement made in footnote 3, page 122.

4. Assuming that the density of states $N(E)$ can be replaced by $N(\zeta)$ within an energy range of a few times kT around ζ, show that the number of electrons with energy greater than ζ is $N(\zeta)kT \log 2$.

8

The Wannier Representation

8.1 Introduction

In quantum mechanics the momentum operator plays the role of the generator of infinitesimal translations; that is, the operator $1 + i\epsilon\hat{\mathbf{n}} \cdot \mathbf{p}$ applied to a state shifts its position by the infinitesimal amount $\epsilon\hbar$ in the direction of the unit vector $\hat{\mathbf{n}}$. (In this discussion, Planck's constant $\hbar$ may be considered to appear for purely dimensional reasons, since instead of the momentum operator we could equally well use any multiple of $\mathbf{p}$, such as $\mathbf{p}/\hbar$.) It follows immediately that for an isolated system, whose Hamiltonian must commute with *all* translations, the momentum is a constant of the motion.

As we have repeatedly seen in previous chapters, the presence of a lattice destroys the constancy of momentum, but introduces instead the *crystal momentum* as a new constant of the motion. The crystal momentum is not a generator of infinitesimal translations, but it does generate the (finite) lattice translations. To see this, we must first define the crystal momentum as an operator, which we can do by defining its action on Bloch states (since the Bloch states form a complete set). Thus we put

$$\mathscr{P}\psi_{n\mathbf{k}}(\mathbf{r}) \equiv \hbar\mathbf{k}\psi_{n\mathbf{k}}(\mathbf{r}). \tag{8.1}$$

In the usual way, any function of the operator is itself an operator defined by

$$F(\mathscr{P})\psi_{n\mathbf{k}}(\mathbf{r}) \equiv F(\hbar\mathbf{k})\psi_{n\mathbf{k}}(\mathbf{r}). \tag{8.2}$$

Consider now an arbitrary wave function $\Psi(\mathbf{r})$, and expand it in Bloch states:

$$\Psi(\mathbf{r}) = \sum_{n\mathbf{k}} A_n(\mathbf{k})\psi_{n\mathbf{k}}(\mathbf{r}). \tag{8.3}$$

Now apply the operator $e^{i\mathscr{P}\cdot\mathbf{R}/\hbar}$, where for the moment $\mathbf{R}$ is *any* constant vector. The result is

$$e^{i\mathscr{P}\cdot\mathbf{R}/\hbar}\Psi(\mathbf{r}) = \sum_{n\mathbf{k}} A_n(\mathbf{k})e^{i\mathbf{k}\cdot\mathbf{R}}\psi_{n\mathbf{k}}(\mathbf{r}) = \sum_{n\mathbf{k}} A_n(\mathbf{k})u_{n\mathbf{k}}(\mathbf{r})e^{i\mathbf{k}\cdot(\mathbf{r}+\mathbf{R})}. \quad (8.4)$$

The new function bears no particular simple relation to the original one, since the exponential part of the Bloch states has been shifted by an amount $\mathbf{R}$, but the periodic part has remained the same. If, however, $\mathbf{R}$ happens to be a lattice translation, then

$$u_{n\mathbf{k}}(\mathbf{r}) = u_{n\mathbf{k}}(\mathbf{r} + \mathbf{R}); \quad (8.5)$$

substituting into Eq. (8.4), we obtain for this case

$$e^{i\mathscr{P}\cdot\mathbf{R}/\hbar}\Psi(\mathbf{r}) = \Psi(\mathbf{r} + \mathbf{R}), \quad (8.6)$$

which shows, since $\Psi(\mathbf{r})$ was an arbitrary function, that $\mathscr{P}$ does indeed generate the lattice translations.

The present chapter will be devoted to the question of whether there exists an operator canonically conjugate to $\mathscr{P}$ and, if so, what its eigenstates are. Note that the situation is rather different from the one encountered in connection with the canonically conjugate variables $\mathbf{p}$ and $\mathbf{r}$; for the eigenvalues of ordinary momentum and position each comprise a continuum extending from $-\infty$ to $+\infty$, whereas the eigenvalues of $\mathscr{P}$ are limited to the Brillouin zone (times $\hbar$). Some intuitive insight may be gained by considering the case of a component L of *angular* momentum: its canonically conjugate partner is the angle of rotation about some axis, and this angle has a limited continuous range from 0 to 2π. As is well known, such a limitation entails a *discrete* set of eigenvalues for L.

Thus we would expect the operator conjugate to $\mathscr{P}$ to have a discrete set of eigenvalues. Insofar as $\mathscr{P}$ has properties similar to momentum, the new operator ought to have properties similar to position; the discreteness of its eigenvalue spectrum then suggests that its eigenstates are partly, but not completely, localized.

8.2 Localized States

As might be suspected, the discrete eigenvalues of the modified position operator will turn out to be the lattice translation vectors, and its eigenstates will be localized to the approximate extent of a primitive cell. There is, of course, no difficulty in constructing a *perfectly* localized state as an expansion in Bloch functions, since the latter comprise a complete set; but for this purpose Bloch functions from all bands must be used. On the other hand, since $\mathscr{P}$ commutes with the band index, it would be nice to find a canonically conjugate variable which does likewise, so that the band index could be treated as though it represented a separate degree of freedom.

We are thus led to seek a representation whose basis states are labeled $|n\mathbf{R}\rangle$, n being the same band index as appears in the Bloch states, whereas the lattice vector $\mathbf{R}$ denotes the cell near which the electron is supposed to be localized; and we require that when $|n\mathbf{R}\rangle$ is expanded in Bloch states, only the band n be used. Furthermore, the function $\langle \mathbf{r} \mid n\mathbf{R} \rangle$, that is, the wave function of the state $|n\mathbf{R}\rangle$ in the $\mathbf{r}$-representation, should depend only on the *difference* $\mathbf{r} - \mathbf{R}$, so that

$$\langle \mathbf{r} + \mathbf{R}_1 \mid n\,\mathbf{R} \rangle = \langle \mathbf{r} \mid n\,\mathbf{R} - \mathbf{R}_1 \rangle; \tag{8.7}$$

this is another way of saying that the various basis states differ only in their location. In Eq. (8.7) $\mathbf{R}_1$ must, of course, be a lattice vector, otherwise the ket on the right side is undefined.

Equation (8.6) in Dirac notation is

$$\langle \mathbf{r} | \, e^{i\mathscr{P}\cdot\mathbf{R}/\hbar} \, | \Psi \rangle = \langle \mathbf{r} + \mathbf{R} \mid \Psi \rangle$$

or, since $|\Psi\rangle$ is arbitrary,

$$\langle \mathbf{r} | \, e^{i\mathscr{P}\cdot\mathbf{R}/\hbar} = \langle \mathbf{r} + \mathbf{R} |. \tag{8.8}$$

Substituting this expression into (8.7) yields

$$\langle \mathbf{r} | \, e^{i\mathscr{P}\cdot\mathbf{R}_1/\hbar} \, | n\,\mathbf{R} \rangle = \langle \mathbf{r} \mid n\,\mathbf{R} - \mathbf{R}_1 \rangle \tag{8.9}$$

for all $\mathbf{r}$, so that

$$|n\,\mathbf{R} + \mathbf{R}_1 \rangle = e^{-i\mathscr{P}\cdot\mathbf{R}_1/\hbar} \, |n\,\mathbf{R} \rangle. \tag{8.10}$$

In order to form a valid basis for a representation, the new states must be orthogonal to each other:

$$\langle n\mathbf{R}_1 \mid n\mathbf{R}_2 \rangle = \sum_{\mathbf{k}} \langle n\mathbf{R}_1 \mid n\mathbf{k} \rangle \langle n\mathbf{k} \mid n\mathbf{R}_2 \rangle = \delta_{\mathbf{R}_1\mathbf{R}_2}, \tag{8.11}$$

where the $|n\mathbf{k}\rangle$'s are Bloch states, and we have used the property

$$\langle n_1\mathbf{R} \mid n_2\mathbf{k} \rangle = 0 \quad \text{if} \quad n_1 \neq n_2 \tag{8.12}$$

which we required above. Letting $\mathbf{R}_2 = \mathbf{R}_1 + \mathbf{R}$, and using Eq. (8.10), Eq. (8.11) becomes

$$\sum_{\mathbf{k}} \langle n\mathbf{R}_1 \mid n\mathbf{k} \rangle \langle n\mathbf{k} | \, e^{-i\mathscr{P}\cdot\mathbf{R}/\hbar} |n\mathbf{R}_1 \rangle = \delta_{\mathbf{R}0};$$

but since $\langle n\mathbf{k} |$ is an eigenstate of $\mathscr{P}$,

$$\sum_{\mathbf{k}} e^{-i\mathbf{k}\cdot\mathbf{R}} \langle n\mathbf{R}_1 \mid n\mathbf{k} \rangle \langle n\mathbf{k} \mid n\mathbf{R}_1 \rangle = \sum_{\mathbf{k}} e^{-i\mathbf{k}\cdot\mathbf{R}} |\langle n\mathbf{k} \mid n\mathbf{R}_1 \rangle|^2 = \delta_{\mathbf{R}0} \tag{8.13}$$

for all $\mathbf{R}_1$.

Multiplying both sides of (8.13) by $e^{i\mathbf{k'}\cdot\mathbf{R}}$, summing over $\mathbf{R}$, and dropping the prime yields

$$|\langle n\mathbf{k} \mid n\mathbf{R}_1\rangle|^2 = \mathcal{N}^{-1} \qquad (8.14)$$

for any $\mathbf{k}$ and any $\mathbf{R}_1$. Thus $|n\mathbf{R}_1\rangle$ has all Bloch states of the band represented with equal intensity.

Equation (8.14) determines the magnitudes, but not the phases, of the elements $\langle n\mathbf{k} \mid n\mathbf{R}\rangle$ of the transformation matrix from the Bloch basis to the new one. The phases are not, however, all independent. Consider the column of the matrix corresponding to $\mathbf{R} = 0$, and define the function $\varphi_n(\mathbf{k})$ by

$$\langle n\mathbf{k} \mid n0\rangle \equiv \mathcal{N}^{-1/2}e^{-i\varphi_n(\mathbf{k})}, \qquad (8.15)$$

which is consistent with (8.14). Then it follows that

$$\langle n\mathbf{k} \mid n\mathbf{R}\rangle = \langle n\mathbf{k}| \, e^{-i\mathscr{P}\cdot\mathbf{R}/\hbar} \, |n0\rangle = \mathcal{N}^{-1/2}e^{-i\varphi_n(\mathbf{k})-i\mathbf{k}\cdot\mathbf{R}}. \qquad (8.16)$$

Thus the new basis is entirely determined by the choice of the function $\varphi_n(\mathbf{k})$.

The wave functions of the new basis in the $\mathbf{r}$-representation are called Wannier functions; we shall denote them by $\beta_n(\mathbf{r} - \mathbf{R})$. According to the above results, they are given by

$$\beta_n(\mathbf{r} - \mathbf{R}) \equiv \langle \mathbf{r} \mid n\mathbf{R}\rangle = \sum_{\mathbf{k}} \langle \mathbf{r} \mid n\mathbf{k}\rangle\langle n\mathbf{k} \mid n\mathbf{R}\rangle$$
$$= \mathcal{N}^{-1/2} \sum_{\mathbf{k}} u_{n\mathbf{k}}(\mathbf{r})e^{-i\varphi_n(\mathbf{k})}e^{i\mathbf{k}\cdot(\mathbf{r}-\mathbf{R})}. \qquad (8.17)$$

8.3   Phases

The definition of the Bloch functions given in Sec. 6.2 leaves, as usual, a phase factor undetermined; that is, if $\psi_{n\mathbf{k}}(\mathbf{r})$ is a complete set of such functions, then $e^{-i\varphi_n(\mathbf{k})}\psi_{n\mathbf{k}}(\mathbf{r})$, where $\varphi_n(\mathbf{k})$ is an arbitrary real function of n and $\mathbf{k}$, is an equally admissible set. Therefore, any discussion of how to choose the phase function in Eq. (8.17) is meaningless until some convention has been established for the phases of the Bloch functions themselves.

Some confusion on this point may be avoided if we write the Bloch function in the form

$$\psi_{n\mathbf{k}}(\mathbf{r}) = \chi_{n\mathbf{k}}(\boldsymbol{\rho})e^{i\mathbf{k}\cdot\mathbf{R}}, \qquad (8.18)$$

where $\mathbf{r}$ has been decomposed, as in Eq. (6.3), into a lattice vector $\mathbf{R}$ plus a vector $\boldsymbol{\rho}$ which lies within the proximity cell. The differential equation satisfied by χ in the interior of the primitive cell is simply

$$\left[-\frac{\hbar^2}{2m} \nabla^2 + U(\mathbf{\rho}) \right] \chi_{n\mathbf{k}}(\mathbf{\rho}) = E_n(\mathbf{k})\chi_{n\mathbf{k}}(\mathbf{\rho}), \tag{8.19}$$

which does not contain $\mathbf{k}$. Instead, $\mathbf{k}$ appears as part of the boundary condition, in that $\psi_{n\mathbf{k}}$ must be continuous even though its exponential part is not. The actual condition is the following. Let $\mathbf{\sigma}$ be a value of $\mathbf{\rho}$ on the surface of the proximity cell. It is shown in Problem 1 that such points can always be grouped into pairs $\mathbf{\sigma}$, $\mathbf{\sigma}'$ which differ by a lattice vector:

$$\mathbf{\sigma}' = \mathbf{\sigma} + \mathbf{R}_\sigma, \tag{8.20}$$

where $\mathbf{R}_\sigma$ is in general different for different $\mathbf{\sigma}$. Now since the point $(\mathbf{R}, \mathbf{\sigma}')$ is the same as the point $(\mathbf{R} + \mathbf{R}_\sigma, \mathbf{\sigma})$, the continuity of ψ demands that

$$\chi_{n\mathbf{k}}(\mathbf{\sigma}')e^{i\mathbf{k} \cdot \mathbf{R}} = \chi_{n\mathbf{k}}(\mathbf{\sigma})e^{i\mathbf{k} \cdot (\mathbf{R}+\mathbf{R}_\sigma)}; \tag{8.21}$$

or

$$\chi_{n\mathbf{k}}(\mathbf{\sigma}') = \chi_{n\mathbf{k}}(\mathbf{\sigma})e^{i\mathbf{k} \cdot \mathbf{R}_\sigma}, \tag{8.22}$$

which is the required boundary condition.

In interpreting the boundary value problem defined by Eqs. (8.19) and (8.22) we can equally well let $\mathbf{k}$ range over all values, not just the ones in the Brillouin zone. Note, however, that the complex number $e^{i\mathbf{k} \cdot \mathbf{R}_\sigma}$ has exactly the same value for two values of $\mathbf{k}$ which differ by a reciprocal lattice vector. Thus at two such points in $\mathbf{k}$-space we would be solving the *same* equation subject to the *same* boundary condition. Let us henceforward assume that a *consistent phase convention* has been chosen for the χ's, where by "consistent" we mean that if the same problem is solved twice, the same phase is assigned (for example, we could require that at some particular point $\mathbf{\rho}_0$ in the proximity cell χ be real and positive). We can then say that not only the eigenvalues $E_n(\mathbf{k})$, *but also the functions* $\chi_{n\mathbf{k}}(\mathbf{\rho})$ *are periodic in extended* $\mathbf{k}$-*space*.

In view of the way in which we have decomposed the vector $\mathbf{r}$, Eq. (8.17) should be appropriately rewritten. Let us use the symbol $\mathbf{R}_0$ for the label of the function β, since $\mathbf{R}$ now stands for the lattice-vector part of $\mathbf{r}$. Then Eq. (8.17) becomes

$$\beta_n(\mathbf{R} + \mathbf{\rho} - \mathbf{R}_0) = \mathcal{N}^{-1/2} \sum_{\mathbf{k}} \chi_{n\mathbf{k}}(\mathbf{\rho})e^{-i\varphi_n(\mathbf{k})}e^{i\mathbf{k} \cdot (\mathbf{R}-\mathbf{R}_0)}. \tag{8.23}$$

From now on, we shall restrict the term "Wannier functions" to functions of the form (8.23) in which not only $\chi_{n\mathbf{k}}(\mathbf{\rho})$ but also the phase factor $e^{-i\varphi_n(\mathbf{k})}$ is a periodic function of $\mathbf{k}$; so that insertion of the phase factor corresponds to a new, but still "consistent," choice of phases for the χ's. We shall now show that it is these functions which have the required localization properties.

8.4 Mean Value of Position

The fact that $e^{-i\varphi_n(\mathbf{k})}$ is periodic in extended $\mathbf{k}$-space means that, for any reciprocal lattice vector $\mathbf{K}$, we must have

$$\varphi_n(\mathbf{k} + \mathbf{K}) = \varphi_n(\mathbf{k}) + 2\pi M_n(\mathbf{k}; \mathbf{K}) \tag{8.24}$$

where $M_n(\mathbf{k}; \mathbf{K})$ is an integer. In fact, if we assume M to be a continuous function of $\mathbf{k}$, then it cannot depend on $\mathbf{k}$ at all, since $\mathbf{k}$ varies through a continuous range while M is always an integer. Accordingly, we can write

$$\varphi_n(\mathbf{k} + \mathbf{K}) = \varphi_n(\mathbf{k}) + 2\pi M_n(\mathbf{K}). \tag{8.25}$$

If we now choose two reciprocal lattice vectors $\mathbf{K}_1$ and $\mathbf{K}_2$ and let $\mathbf{K}$ in Eq. (8.25) be equal to $\mathbf{K}_1 + \mathbf{K}_2$, we find that

$$2\pi M_n(\mathbf{K}_1 + \mathbf{K}_2) = 2\pi M_n(\mathbf{K}_1) + 2\pi M_n(\mathbf{K}_2), \tag{8.26}$$

so that $2\pi M_n$ is *a linear function of* $\mathbf{K}$ *which is equal to* 2π *times an integer for every reciprocal lattice vector* $\mathbf{K}$. This implies, according to the material of Chapter 2, that

$$2\pi M_n(\mathbf{K}) = \mathbf{K} \cdot \mathbf{R}_n, \tag{8.27}$$

where $\mathbf{R}_n$ is a lattice vector; in other words,

$$\varphi_n(\mathbf{k} + \mathbf{K}) = \varphi_n(\mathbf{k}) + \mathbf{K} \cdot \mathbf{R}_n. \tag{8.28}$$

Let a new function $\lambda_n(\mathbf{k})$ be defined by

$$\varphi_n(\mathbf{k}) \equiv \lambda_n(\mathbf{k}) + \mathbf{k} \cdot \mathbf{R}_n; \tag{8.29}$$

substituting into Eq. (8.28), we then find that

$$\lambda_n(\mathbf{k} + \mathbf{K}) = \lambda_n(\mathbf{k}) \tag{8.30}$$

for any $\mathbf{K}$. Thus *the most general admissible* $\varphi_n(\mathbf{k})$ *consists of a periodic function of* $\mathbf{k}$ *plus the scalar product of* $\mathbf{k}$ *with some lattice vector.*

The form of $\varphi_n(\mathbf{k})$ as given by Eq. (8.29) changes Eq. (8.23) into

$$\beta_n(\mathbf{R} + \boldsymbol{\rho} - \mathbf{R}_0) = \mathcal{N}^{-\frac{1}{2}} \sum_{\mathbf{k}} \chi_{n\mathbf{k}}(\boldsymbol{\rho}) e^{-i\lambda_n(\mathbf{k})} e^{i\mathbf{k} \cdot (\mathbf{R} - \mathbf{R}_0 - \mathbf{R}_n)}. \tag{8.31}$$

It is thus clear that the effect of the linear term in (8.29) is to shift the whole Wannier function in space by an amount $\mathbf{R}_n$. This fact suggests a simple criterion for the choice of the vector $\mathbf{R}_n$: we simply require that the mean value of $\mathbf{r}$ in a Wannier state lie in the proximity cell belonging to $\mathbf{R}_0$. Thus, for the first time, the labeling of the Wannier states becomes physically meaningful. The remaining part $\lambda_n(\mathbf{k})$ of the phase function must be a periodic function of $\mathbf{k}$; we shall discuss later what criteria might be used for its selection.

8.5 Asymptotic Behavior of Wannier Functions

In Eq. (8.31), we can absorb the factor $e^{i\mathbf{k}\cdot\mathbf{R}_n}$ into $\chi_{n\mathbf{k}}(\boldsymbol{\rho})$, representing a new (but still "consistent") choice of phases such as to satisfy the criterion of the previous section. We now introduce two more changes into Eq. (8.31). First, note that the Bloch functions have heretofore been assumed to be normalized over the volume of the whole crystal, so that, from Eq. (8.18).

$$\mathcal{N}\int |\chi_{n\mathbf{k}}(\boldsymbol{\rho})|^2 \, d^3\rho = 1, \tag{8.32}$$

where the integral is over a primitive cell. By making the replacement

$$\mathcal{N}^{1/2}\chi_{n\mathbf{k}}(\boldsymbol{\rho}) \to \chi_{n\mathbf{k}}(\boldsymbol{\rho}), \tag{8.33}$$

the normalization integral becomes simply

$$\int |\chi_{n\mathbf{k}}(\boldsymbol{\rho})|^2 \, d^3\rho = 1. \tag{8.34}$$

Second, the sum in Eq. (8.31) may be written as an integral, since $\mathcal{N}$ is assumed large. The expression for the Wannier function then becomes

$$\beta_n(\mathbf{R} + \boldsymbol{\rho} - \mathbf{R}_0) = \frac{V/\mathcal{N}}{(2\pi)^3}\int \chi_{n\mathbf{k}}(\boldsymbol{\rho})e^{-i\lambda_n(\mathbf{k})}e^{i\mathbf{k}\cdot(\mathbf{R}-\mathbf{R}_0)} \, d^3k. \tag{8.35}$$

Equation (8.35) shows explicitly that β is independent of the size of the crystal.

Consider now a particular β, say the one for $\mathbf{R}_0 = 0$, and multiply it by some power μ of the vector $\mathbf{R}$:

$$\mathbf{R}^\mu \beta_n(\mathbf{R} + \boldsymbol{\rho}) = \frac{V/\mathcal{N}}{(2\pi)^3}\int \chi_{n\mathbf{k}}(\boldsymbol{\rho})e^{-i\lambda_n(\mathbf{k})}\mathbf{R}^\mu e^{i\mathbf{k}\cdot\mathbf{R}} \, d^3k$$

$$= \frac{V/\mathcal{N}}{(2\pi)^3}\int \chi_{n\mathbf{k}}(\boldsymbol{\rho})e^{-i\lambda_n(\mathbf{k})}\left(\frac{\nabla_\mathbf{k}}{i}\right)^\mu e^{i\mathbf{k}\cdot\mathbf{R}} \, d^3k$$

$$= \frac{V/\mathcal{N}}{(2\pi)^3}i^\mu\int e^{i\mathbf{k}\cdot\mathbf{R}}\nabla_\mathbf{k}^\mu \chi_{n\mathbf{k}}(\boldsymbol{\rho})e^{-i\lambda_n(\mathbf{k})} \, d^3k, \tag{8.36}$$

where the periodicity in $\mathbf{k}$ of the various parts of the integrand allows us to drop the surface terms resulting from the partial integration. The integral in Eq. (8.36) is just the $\mathbf{R}$th coefficient of the Fourier series expansion of the periodic function of $\mathbf{k}$ which appears in the integrand, and therefore approaches zero for large $\mathbf{R}$ provided the function is reasonably well behaved. In particular, if the band n is nondegenerate, then χ is an analytic function of $\mathbf{k}$ and all its derivatives exist. We therefore conclude that *the Wannier functions of a nondegenerate band vanish at infinity faster than any finite power of* $\mathbf{R}$. The case of a band which has points, lines, or planes of degeneracy with another band is, however, more complicated, since degeneracy generally implies discontinuity in χ as a function of $\mathbf{k}$ (cf. Problem 4).

8.6 Spatial Extent of Wannier Functions

The mean-square spatial extent of a Wannier function is given by $\langle \mathbf{r}^2 \rangle - \langle \mathbf{r} \rangle^2$, where the angular brackets denote expectation values. Considering the particular function labeled by $\mathbf{R}_0 = 0$, we know that $\langle \mathbf{r} \rangle$ lies within the central proximity cell, and is therefore at most of the order of a lattice spacing; furthermore, the difference between $\langle \mathbf{r}^2 \rangle$ and $\langle \mathbf{R}^2 \rangle$ is appreciable only if the root-mean-square value of $\mathbf{r}$ (or $\mathbf{R}$) is of the order of a lattice spacing or less. If, therefore, we are prepared to neglect quantities of the order of a lattice spacing, we may use as a measure of the mean square spread of a Wannier function the expectation value of $\mathbf{R}^2$ in the state labeled by $\mathbf{R}_0 = 0$.

From Eq. (8.35), this quantity is given by

$$
\begin{aligned}
\langle \mathbf{R}^2 \rangle_{n0} &= \frac{(V/\mathcal{N})^2}{(2\pi)^6} \sum_{\mathbf{R}} \int d^3\rho \, d^3k \, d^3k' \chi^*_{n\mathbf{k}}(\boldsymbol{\rho}) e^{i\lambda_n(\mathbf{k})} e^{-i\mathbf{k}\cdot\mathbf{R}} \mathbf{R}^2 \\
&\quad \times \chi_{n\mathbf{k}'}(\boldsymbol{\rho}) e^{-i\lambda_n(\mathbf{k}')} e^{i\mathbf{k}'\cdot\mathbf{R}} \\
&= \frac{(V/\mathcal{N})^2}{(2\pi)^6} \sum_{\mathbf{R}} \int d^3\rho \, d^3k \, d^3k' \chi^*_{n\mathbf{k}}(\boldsymbol{\rho}) \chi_{n\mathbf{k}'}(\boldsymbol{\rho}) e^{i\lambda_n(\mathbf{k})-i\lambda_n(\mathbf{k}')} \\
&\quad \times [\nabla_{\mathbf{k}} e^{-i\mathbf{k}\cdot\mathbf{R}}] \cdot [\nabla_{\mathbf{k}'} e^{i\mathbf{k}'\cdot\mathbf{R}}] \\
&= \frac{(V/\mathcal{N})^2}{(2\pi)^6} \int d^3\rho \, d^3k \, d^3k' [\nabla_{\mathbf{k}} \chi^*_{n\mathbf{k}}(\boldsymbol{\rho}) e^{i\lambda_n(\mathbf{k})}] \\
&\quad \cdot [\nabla_{\mathbf{k}'} \chi_{n\mathbf{k}'}(\boldsymbol{\rho}) e^{-i\lambda_n(\mathbf{k}')}] \sum_{\mathbf{R}} e^{i(\mathbf{k}'-\mathbf{k})\cdot\mathbf{R}}.
\end{aligned}
\tag{8.37}
$$

The last sum is one which we have encountered a number of times before and know to be equal to $\mathcal{N}\delta_{\mathbf{k}\mathbf{k}'}$. This form is not, however, suitable for the present calculation, in which the sum over $\mathbf{k}$-values has been replaced by an integral. Instead, we must write

$$
\sum_{\mathbf{R}} e^{i(\mathbf{k}'-\mathbf{k})\cdot\mathbf{R}} = B\delta(\mathbf{k}' - \mathbf{k}),
\tag{8.38}
$$

where δ is a Dirac delta-function. The constant B is determined by the condition

$$\sum_{\mathbf{k}} \sum_{\mathbf{R}} e^{i(\mathbf{k}'-\mathbf{k}) \cdot \mathbf{R}} = \sum_{\mathbf{k}} \mathcal{N} \delta_{\mathbf{kk}'} = \mathcal{N}, \tag{8.39}$$

which in integral notation becomes

$$\frac{V}{(2\pi)^3} \int d^3k \sum_{\mathbf{R}} e^{i(\mathbf{k}'-\mathbf{k}) \cdot \mathbf{R}} = \frac{V}{(2\pi)^3} \int d^3k B \,\delta(\mathbf{k}' - \mathbf{k}) = \mathcal{N}; \tag{8.40}$$

it then follows that

$$B = \frac{(2\pi)^3}{(V/\mathcal{N})}. \tag{8.41}$$

Substituting (8.38) and (8.41) into (8.37), we obtain

$$\langle \mathbf{R}^2 \rangle_{n0} = \frac{V/\mathcal{N}}{(2\pi)^3} \int d^3\rho \, d^3k \, |\nabla_{\mathbf{k}} \chi_{n\mathbf{k}}(\boldsymbol{\rho}) e^{-i\lambda_n(\mathbf{k})}|^2. \tag{8.42}$$

We shall now show that there exists a unique choice for the phase function $\lambda_n(\mathbf{k})$ which minimizes $\langle \mathbf{R}^2 \rangle_{n0}$. For this purpose, we write Eq. (8.42) more explicitly:

$$\langle \mathbf{R}^2 \rangle_{n0} = \frac{V/\mathcal{N}}{(2\pi)^3} \int d^3k \{P(\mathbf{k}) + 2\mathbf{Q}(\mathbf{k}) \cdot \nabla_{\mathbf{k}} \lambda_n(\mathbf{k}) + |\nabla_{\mathbf{k}} \lambda_n(\mathbf{k})|^2\}, \tag{8.43}$$

where

$$P(\mathbf{k}) \equiv \int d^3\rho \, |\nabla_{\mathbf{k}} \chi_{n\mathbf{k}}(\boldsymbol{\rho})|^2, \tag{8.44}$$

$$2\mathbf{Q}(\mathbf{k}) \equiv \int d^3\rho \, i[\chi_{n\mathbf{k}}^*(\boldsymbol{\rho}) \, \nabla_{\mathbf{k}} \chi_{n\mathbf{k}}(\boldsymbol{\rho}) - \chi_{n\mathbf{k}}(\boldsymbol{\rho}) \, \nabla_{\mathbf{k}} \chi_{n\mathbf{k}}^*(\boldsymbol{\rho})], \tag{8.45}$$

and the normalization of the χ's, Eq. (8.34), has been used.

We are thus faced with the variational problem of choosing $\lambda_n(\mathbf{k})$ so as to minimize the integral in Eq. (8.43). The Euler-Lagrange equation for this integral is

$$\nabla_{\mathbf{k}} \cdot [\mathbf{Q}(\mathbf{k}) + \nabla_{\mathbf{k}} \lambda_n(\mathbf{k})] = 0 \tag{8.46}$$

or

$$\nabla_{\mathbf{k}}^2 \lambda_n(\mathbf{k}) = -\nabla_{\mathbf{k}} \cdot \mathbf{Q}(\mathbf{k}). \tag{8.47}$$

The last equation is equivalent to an electrostatic problem in which we are given a charge distribution $\nabla_{\mathbf{k}} \cdot \mathbf{Q}(\mathbf{k})$ which is periodic in $\mathbf{k}$-space and ask for the electrostatic potential $\lambda_n(\mathbf{k})$ subject to the boundary condition that it too be periodic in $\mathbf{k}$-space; it is well known that the solution to this problem is unique (except for a trivial additive constant).

It is not possible to calculate the actual minimum value of $\langle \mathbf{R}^2 \rangle_{n0}$ without knowing the Bloch functions explicitly. On the other hand, given that a minimum value exists, it is almost surely of the order of a lattice spacing on purely dimensional grounds.

8.7 The Operator **R**

The previous sections have shown that a set of states is completely defined by the following set of requirements:

a. the states are to be made up of Bloch states without mixing of bands and be orthogonal to each other;

b. the states are to be labeled by lattice vectors and be obtainable from one another by corresponding lattice translation operators;

c. the mean value of **r** in each state is to lie within the proximity cell belonging to the label vector $\mathbf{R}_0$;

d. the mean value of $(\mathbf{R} - \mathbf{R}_0)^2$ is to be a minimum.

We have also seen that these states, which we shall henceforth refer to simply as Wannier states, have wave functions which are localized in the vicinity of their label vectors. The fact that they form a complete set (see Problem 2) then suggests that we define a *Wannier position operator* **R** as the operator of which the Wannier states are eigenstates, and whose eigenvalues are the respective label vectors. The definition is expressed formally as

$$\mathbf{R} \equiv \sum_{n\mathbf{R}_0} |n\,\mathbf{R}_0\rangle \mathbf{R}_0 \langle n\,\mathbf{R}_0|. \tag{8.48}$$

Equation (8.48) is not, however, acceptable because of the periodic boundary conditions which we have imposed. The reader will recall that *all* Bloch states are periodic with periods $L\mathbf{a}_1$, $M\mathbf{a}_2$, $N\mathbf{a}_3$, so that a Wannier function is really only "locally localized," repeating in every "large cell" of the (infinite) crystal. This fact makes the eigenvalues $\mathbf{R}_0$ in Eq. (8.48) inherently multiple-valued, leaving the operator undefined. The artifice of letting L, M, and N go to infinity is questionable in that the very great size of a crystal does not preclude an electron being near its surface; whereas any attempt to bring in the surface in a physically realistic way leads immediately to a loss of the Bloch basis as energy eigenstates.

A possible approach to this difficulty is to define a function $\tilde{\mathbf{R}}_0$ of $\mathbf{R}_0$ which we may call the "reduced lattice vector." The function is to be defined so that for $\mathbf{R}_0$ reasonably small $\tilde{\mathbf{R}}_0$ is equal to $\mathbf{R}_0$, but at the same time $\tilde{\mathbf{R}}_0$ *is* periodic in the "large cells." Letting

$$\mathbf{R}_0 = l\mathbf{a}_1 + m\mathbf{a}_2 + n\mathbf{a}_3 \tag{8.49}$$

$$\tilde{\mathbf{R}}_0 = \tilde{l}\mathbf{a}_1 + \tilde{m}\mathbf{a}_2 + \tilde{n}\mathbf{a}_3, \tag{8.50}$$

we show in Fig. 8.1 the type of dependence of $\tilde{l}$ on l which we desire; the other two components are to behave in a similar way. Now, it is well known that such a function can be constructed as a trigonometric series:

$$\tilde{l} = \sum_{\mu} A_{\mu} \sin \frac{2\pi\mu l}{L}.$$ (8.51)

The more terms are included in (8.51), the closer the region where $\tilde{l} \approx l$ can be made to approach the boundaries of the large cell; but no matter

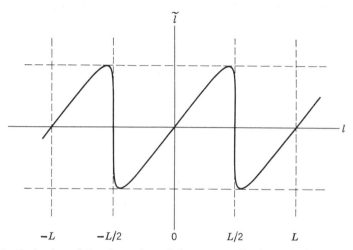

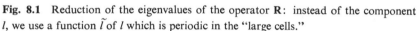

Fig. 8.1 Reduction of the eigenvalues of the operator **R**: instead of the component l, we use a function $\tilde{l}$ of l which is periodic in the "large cells."

how many terms are used we must have

$$\sum_{\mu} A_{\mu} \frac{2\pi\mu}{L} = 1$$ (8.52)

in order to obtain the correct behavior near $l = 0$. We may now define the Wannier position operator as

$$\mathbf{R} \equiv \sum_{n\mathbf{R}_0} |n\mathbf{R}_0\rangle \tilde{\mathbf{R}}_0 \langle n\mathbf{R}_0|.$$ (8.53)

The sum is, of course, over *one* large cell.

8.8 Matrix of R in Bloch Representation

Equation (8.53) is equivalent to the matrix equation

$$\langle n'\mathbf{R}_0'| \, \mathbf{R} \, |n\mathbf{R}_0\rangle = \tilde{\mathbf{R}}_0 \, \delta_{nn'} \, \delta_{\mathbf{R}_0\mathbf{R}_0'}.$$ (8.54)

To transform into the Bloch representation, we use the transformation matrix, Eq. (8.16):[1]

$$\langle n'\mathbf{k}'|\ \mathbf{R}\ |n\mathbf{k}\rangle = \sum_{n''\mathbf{R}_0} \sum_{n'''\mathbf{R}_0'} \langle n'\mathbf{k}'\ |\ n''\,\mathbf{R}_0\rangle\langle n''\mathbf{R}_0|\ \mathbf{R}\ |n'''\,\mathbf{R}_0'\rangle\langle n'''\,\mathbf{R}_0'\ |\ n\mathbf{k}\rangle$$

$$= \mathscr{N}^{-1}\delta_{nn'}\sum_{\mathbf{R}_0}\tilde{\mathbf{R}}_0 e^{i(\mathbf{k}-\mathbf{k}')\cdot\mathbf{R}_0}. \tag{8.55}$$

Consider now the first component of $\mathbf{R}$. According to Eq. (8.55) and (8.51)

$$\langle n'\mathbf{k}'|\ l\mathbf{a}_1\ |n\mathbf{k}\rangle = \mathbf{a}_1 \mathscr{N}^{-1}\delta_{nn'}\sum_{\mu\mathbf{R}_0} A_\mu \sin\frac{2\pi\mu l}{L}\, e^{i(\mathbf{k}-\mathbf{k}')\cdot\mathbf{R}_0}. \tag{8.56}$$

The sum over $\mathbf{R}_0$ is, of course, a triple sum over l, m, and n, which factors into a product of three single sums. For the allowed $\mathbf{k}$-values we put, as in Eq. (2.21),

$$\mathbf{k} = \frac{r_1}{L}\,\mathbf{b}^1 + \frac{r_2}{M}\,\mathbf{b}^2 + \frac{r_3}{N}\,\mathbf{b}^3, \tag{8.57}$$

$$\mathbf{k}' = \frac{r_1'}{L}\,\mathbf{b}^1 + \frac{r_2'}{M}\,\mathbf{b}^2 + \frac{r_3'}{N}\,\mathbf{b}^3. \tag{8.58}$$

The sums over m and n are then equal respectively to $M\delta_{r_2 r_2'}$ and $N\delta_{r_3 r_3'}$. The sum over l is, for a particular μ,

$$\frac{A_\mu}{2i}\sum_l e^{2\pi i(r_1-r_1')l/L}[e^{2\pi i\mu/L} - e^{-2\pi i\mu/L}] = \frac{A_\mu L}{2i}(\delta_{r_1',r_1+\mu} - \delta_{r_1',r_1-\mu}). \tag{8.59}$$

Thus, since $LMN = \mathscr{N}$, the matrix element becomes

$$\langle n'\mathbf{k}'|\ l\mathbf{a}_1\ |n\mathbf{k}\rangle = \frac{\mathbf{a}_1\,\delta_{nn'}}{2i}\sum_\mu A_\mu(\delta_{\mathbf{k}',\mathbf{k}+(\mu/L)\mathbf{b}^1} - \delta_{\mathbf{k}',\mathbf{k}-(\mu/L)\mathbf{b}^1}). \tag{8.60}$$

Similar expressions hold for the other two components of $\mathbf{R}$. It is seen from Eq. (8.59) that the values of $\mathbf{k}$ which the operator $\mathbf{R}$ connects lie very close to each other, but that the diagonal elements of $\mathbf{R}$ are zero.

8.9 Electrons in the Interior of the Crystal

Great simplification of Eq. (8.60) can be achieved if we assume that the electron is known to be well in the interior of the crystal. Note that this assumption does not really represent a new approximation, since in our formalism the surfaces of the crystal are represented by periodic

[1] We no longer write the explicit phase factor $e^{-i\varphi_n(\mathbf{k})}$, assuming it to have been chosen according to the criteria of the preceding sections and then incorporated into the χ's.

boundary conditions, and periodic boundary conditions are certainly absurd as a physical model. Thus, in using them we are already limiting ourselves to problems in which the surface is, in fact, unimportant.

Suppose, then that the electron resides in a region around the origin which is small compared to the size of the crystal. Its wave function is then a superposition of Wannier functions whose label vectors are small compared to a "large cell." As we saw in Sec. 8.2, the wave function of a Wannier state in the Bloch representation is

$$\langle n\mathbf{k} \mid n\mathbf{R}_0 \rangle = \mathcal{N}^{-\frac{1}{2}} e^{-i\mathbf{k}\cdot\mathbf{R}_0} = \mathcal{N}^{-\frac{1}{2}} \exp\left[-2\pi i\left(\frac{r_1 l}{L} + \frac{r_2 m}{M} + \frac{r_3 n}{N}\right)\right],$$

(8.61)

where the notation of (8.49) and (8.57) is used. It is clear from Eq. (8.61) that if l is much less than L, as we are assuming, then $\langle n\mathbf{k} \mid n\mathbf{R}_0 \rangle$ is a slowly varying function of r_1; that is, r_1 must change by an amount much greater than unity before the function changes appreciably. If now $|\psi\rangle$ is any superposition of such Wannier states, it must still be true that $\langle n\mathbf{k} \mid \psi \rangle$, viewed as a function of $\mathbf{k}$, varies slowly on the scale on which the allowed values of $\mathbf{k}$ are spaced.

On the other hand, the limitation to the interior of the crystal means that the trigonometric series (8.51) need only contain a few terms, so that $A_\mu = 0$ except for μ of the order of unity.

Suppose now that we take some state $|\psi\rangle$ which satisfies these criteria, apply the first component of the operator $\mathbf{R}$, and ask for the wave function of the resulting state in the Bloch representation:

$$\langle n\mathbf{k}| \, l\mathbf{a}_1 \, |\psi\rangle = \sum_{\mathbf{k}'} \langle n\mathbf{k}| \, l\mathbf{a}_1 \mid n\mathbf{k}'\rangle\langle n\mathbf{k}' \mid \psi\rangle$$

$$= \frac{\mathbf{a}_1}{2i} \sum_{\mathbf{k}'\mu} A_\mu (\delta_{\mathbf{k},\mathbf{k}'+(\mu/L)\mathbf{b}^1} - \delta_{\mathbf{k},\mathbf{k}'-(\mu/L)\mathbf{b}^1})\langle n\mathbf{k}' \mid \psi\rangle$$

$$= \frac{\mathbf{a}_1}{2i} \sum_{\mu} A_\mu \left(\left\langle n\mathbf{k} - \frac{\mu}{L}\mathbf{b}^1 \mid \psi \right\rangle - \left\langle n\mathbf{k} + \frac{\mu}{L}\mathbf{b}^1 \mid \psi \right\rangle\right)$$

$$= i\mathbf{a}_1 \sum_{\mu} \frac{A_\mu \mu}{L} \mathbf{b}^1 \cdot \nabla_{\mathbf{k}}\langle n\mathbf{k} \mid \psi\rangle,$$

(8.62)

where in the last step the slow variation of $\langle n\mathbf{k} \mid \psi \rangle$ has been used. With the aid of Eq. (8.52), Eq. (8.62) becomes

$$\langle n\mathbf{k}| \, l\mathbf{a}_1 \, |\psi\rangle = \frac{i}{2\pi} \mathbf{a}_1 \mathbf{b}^1 \cdot \nabla_{\mathbf{k}}\langle n\mathbf{k} \mid \psi\rangle.$$

(8.63)

It is easy to extend (8.63) to the other two components of $\mathbf{R}$. Using the identity

$$\mathbf{a}_1 \mathbf{b}^1 + \mathbf{a}_2 \mathbf{b}^2 + \mathbf{a}_3 \mathbf{b}^3 = 2\pi\mathbf{I},$$

(8.64)

where **I** is the unit dyadic, we thus obtain the important result

$$\langle nk| \ \mathbf{R} \ |\psi\rangle = i\nabla_{\mathbf{k}}\langle nk \ | \ \psi\rangle \tag{8.65}$$

for any $|\psi\rangle$ localized in the interior of the crystal.

8.10 Wannier Velocity

The operator which represents the rate of change of **R** is given by

$$\dot{\mathbf{R}} \equiv \frac{i}{\hbar} [H, \mathbf{R}], \tag{8.66}$$

where H is the Hamiltonian. If $|\psi\rangle$ is a state which satisfies the criteria of the previous section, then

$$\begin{aligned}
\langle nk| \ H\mathbf{R} \ |\psi\rangle &= E_n(\mathbf{k})\langle nk| \ \mathbf{R} \ |\psi\rangle \\
&= E_n(\mathbf{k})i\nabla_{\mathbf{k}}\langle nk \ | \ \psi\rangle;
\end{aligned} \tag{8.67}$$

whereas $\quad \langle nk| \ \mathbf{R}H \ |\psi\rangle = i\nabla_{\mathbf{k}}\langle nk| \ H \ |\psi\rangle$

$$\begin{aligned}
&= i\nabla_{\mathbf{k}}\{E_n(\mathbf{k})\langle nk \ | \ \psi\rangle\} \\
&= \{i\nabla_{\mathbf{k}}E_n(\mathbf{k})\}\langle nk \ | \ \psi\rangle + E_n(\mathbf{k})i\nabla_{\mathbf{k}}\langle nk \ | \ \psi\rangle. \tag{8.68}
\end{aligned}$$

In Eq. (8.68) we have used the fact that if $\langle nk \ | \ \psi\rangle$ is a slow function of **k**, then $\langle nk| \ H \ |\psi\rangle$ must be also; this follows from the relation

$$\langle nk| \ H \ |\psi\rangle = E_n(\mathbf{k})\langle nk \ | \ \psi\rangle \tag{8.69}$$

and the obvious observation that $E_n(\mathbf{k})$ varies slowly on the scale on which allowed **k**-values are spaced. From (8.67) and (8.68) we obtain

$$\langle nk| \ \dot{\mathbf{R}} \ |\psi\rangle = \left\{\frac{1}{\hbar}\nabla_{\mathbf{k}}E_n(\mathbf{k})\right\} \langle nk \ | \ \psi\rangle. \tag{8.70}$$

It appears from Eq. (8.70) that in the Bloch representation $\dot{\mathbf{R}}$ is simply a multiplicative operator, i.e., that it is represented by a diagonal matrix. That such is not the case can be seen from the fact that in this representation H is diagonal while **R** has, according to Eq. (8.60), *no* diagonal elements. It follows that neither $H\mathbf{R}$ nor $\mathbf{R}H$ (nor, consequently, $\dot{\mathbf{R}}$) can have any diagonal elements at all. Indeed, we should not expect a *pure* Bloch state to have any expectation value of velocity; for the way we have "reduced" **R** in Sec. 8.7 amounts to requiring that an electron which reaches a crystal boundary shoot back and re-enter the crystal from the opposite face. Clearly, the average velocity in such an orbit is zero.

Actually, there is nothing wrong with Eq. (8.70) as it stands; the mathematically incorrect conclusion that the $\langle n\mathbf{k}|$'s are eigenstates of $\mathbf{R}$ could be drawn only by cancelling $|\psi\rangle$ from both sides of the equation, and such a step would be valid only if $|\psi\rangle$ represented a completely arbitrary ket, rather than being constrained to the interior of the crystal. Physically, on the other hand, it is only such wave packets that have any meaning anyway, and to think of the Bloch states as eigenstates of velocity is entirely justified; the only way one could get into trouble thereby is in connection with electrons near the surface of the crystal, in which case the whole formalism based on periodic boundary conditions would break down. Note, incidentally, that the "eigenvalue" of $\dot{\mathbf{R}}$ indicated by Eq. (8.70) corresponds exactly to the average velocity of Eq. (6.14).

PROBLEMS

1. Show that for every point on the surface of a primitive cell there exists another point on the surface such that the vector connecting them is a lattice vector. This is true for any of the possible parallelepipedal cells as well as for the proximity cell.

2. Given that the Bloch functions form a complete set, prove that the Wannier functions also do.

3. Find the Wannier functions corresponding to the "tight-binding limit" defined in Problem 4 of Chapter 6. Make sure that you choose the phases according to the requirements of Secs. 8.4 and 8.6.

4. Discuss the Wannier functions for the simple cubic empty lattice. Can you show how the slow fall-off as $R \to \infty$ is connected with the existence of planes of degeneracy?

9

Effective-mass Theory

9.1 Introduction

In this chapter we shall study the way in which the crystal momentum changes with time when the periodicity of the crystal is violated. For this purpose we shall find the definition (8.1) of the operator $\mathscr{P}$ to be inadequate, for according to that definition the eigenvalue of $\mathscr{P}$ suffers a discontinuous change when an electron crosses a zone boundary, even though the eigenfunction remains perfectly continuous. To tolerate such an unphysical discontinuity is to ask for grave analytical trouble in an attempt to discuss the physical variation of $\mathscr{P}$ with time.

Before we get lost, however, in the formal procedure of "reducing" $\mathscr{P}$ (somewhat along the lines by which $\mathbf{R}$ was reduced in Sec. 8.7), it is worth asking why no analytical trouble appeared when we used the definition (8.1) in Chapter 8. The reason, as the reader may verify, is that $\mathscr{P}$ always appeared in an exponential dotted into a lattice vector, so that if the eigenvalue jumped by a reciprocal lattice vector, nothing changed. In fact the original definition of $\mathscr{P}$ was in terms of the eigenvalues of the translation operators, which have none of the discontinuity. We conclude that the complications in describing the variation of $\mathscr{P}$ with time are rooted in the fact that it is simply not a very good variable; if we were willing to deal with a complex unimodular multiplicative property of electrons instead of insisting on a real additive vector momentum, these complications would never arise.[1]

---

[1] The mariner's compass is an interesting example of a cyclic scale which joins back on itself without a singularity. By and large, however, we seem to insist on using linear scales for cyclic variables, as a result of which such bizarre singularities as the International Date Line are created. Poor as we seem to be at thinking in a circle, it is not surprising that thinking in a three-dimensional torus does not come naturally.

The situation is rather different from what we encountered in the previous chapter in connection with the vector **R**. There, steps had to be taken to eliminate the ill effects of the bogus periodicity of the boundary conditions; this could be accomplished by restricting the electron to being well in the interior of the crystal. On the other hand, the periodicity of Bloch functions in **k**-space is real; conversely, restricting our theory to electrons well in the interior of the Brillouin zone would make it useless for many purposes.

We shall now show that a generalization of the method of Sec. 8.7 will work under a weaker restriction, namely, that the electron's wave function be well localized in a small fraction of the Brillouin zone, *though not necessarily near its center.* (Afterwards, the reader will be able to convince himself that even a linear combination of a few states, each one of which is strongly localized near some point of the zone, can be treated in a similar way.) Many states encountered in practice satisfy this criterion; a single state is obviously the extreme example.

9.2 The Operator $\mathscr{P}$ in the Wannier Representation

Assuming that the electron's wave function is localized near a point **k*** in the zone, we simply construct the trigonometric series corresponding to (8.51) around the point **k***. Figure 9.1 shows how such a reduced wave vector $\tilde{\mathbf{k}}$ would depend on **k** in a one-dimensional case. Mathematically, we write[2]

$$\tilde{\mathbf{k}} \equiv \mathbf{k}^* + \sum_{\sigma=1}^{3}\sum_{\mu} B_{\mu\sigma}\mathbf{b}^{\sigma} \sin \left[(\mathbf{k} - \mathbf{k}^*) \cdot \mu \mathbf{a}_{\sigma} \right], \tag{9.1}$$

where the three $\mathbf{a}_\sigma$'s and the three $\mathbf{b}^\sigma$'s are the primitive vectors of the direct and reciprocal lattice. The expression (9.1) has the correct behavior near $\mathbf{k} = \mathbf{k}^*$ provided that

$$\sum_{\mu} B_{\mu\sigma}\mu = \frac{1}{2\pi} \tag{9.2}$$

for each of the three values of σ.

Using Eq. (9.1) we define the operator $\mathscr{P}$ by

$$\mathscr{P} \equiv \sum_{n\mathbf{k}} |n\mathbf{k}\rangle \, \hbar\tilde{\mathbf{k}} \, \langle n\mathbf{k}|. \tag{9.3}$$

Suppose now that we have the wave function $\langle n\mathbf{R}_0 \mid \psi \rangle$ of some state in the

---

[2] In the corresponding discussion of **R** we worked with a single component, viz. $l\mathbf{a}_1$. Equation (9.1) is merely a tricky way of writing all three components simultaneously.

Wannier representation; then the wave function $\langle n\mathbf{R}_0| \mathscr{P} |\psi\rangle$ is given by

$$\frac{1}{\hbar} \langle n\mathbf{R}_0| \mathscr{P} |\psi\rangle = \sum_{\mathbf{k}} \langle n\mathbf{R}_0 | n\mathbf{k}\rangle$$

$$\times \{\mathbf{k}^* + \sum_{\sigma\mu} B_{\mu\sigma}\mathbf{b}^{\sigma} \sin[(\mathbf{k} - \mathbf{k}^*)\cdot\mu\mathbf{a}_{\sigma}]\} \langle n\mathbf{k} | \psi\rangle. \quad (9.4)$$

The first term in the braces is a constant and thus sums back to $\mathbf{k}^*\langle n\mathbf{R}_0 | \psi\rangle$. In the second term we expand the sine in exponentials and note that, for example,

$$\langle n\mathbf{R}_0 | n\mathbf{k}\rangle e^{i(\mathbf{k}-\mathbf{k}^*)\cdot\mu\mathbf{a}_{\sigma}} = e^{-i\mathbf{k}^*\cdot\mu\mathbf{a}_{\sigma}}\langle n\mathbf{R}_0 + \mu\mathbf{a}_{\sigma} | n\mathbf{k}\rangle \quad (9.5)$$

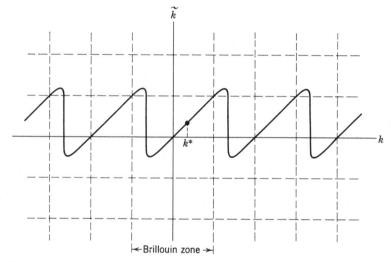

Fig 9.1 Reduction of the eigenvalues of $\mathscr{P}$ for the case in which an electron is localized in the Brillouin zone near a point $\mathbf{k}^*$.

as is seen from Eq. (8.61). Thus we obtain

$$\frac{1}{\hbar} \langle n\mathbf{R}_0| \mathscr{P} |\psi\rangle = \mathbf{k}^*\langle n\mathbf{R}_0 | \psi\rangle + \frac{1}{2i}\sum_{\sigma\mu} B_{\mu\sigma}\mathbf{b}^{\sigma}$$

$$\times \{e^{-i\mathbf{k}^*\cdot\mu\mathbf{a}_{\sigma}}\langle n\mathbf{R}_0 + \mu\mathbf{a}_{\sigma} | \psi\rangle - e^{i\mathbf{k}^*\cdot\mu\mathbf{a}_{\sigma}}\langle n\mathbf{R}_0 - \mu\mathbf{a}_{\sigma} | \psi\rangle\}. \quad (9.6)$$

Now the wave function of a Bloch state $|n\mathbf{k}\rangle$ in the Wannier representation is

$$\langle n\mathbf{R}_0 | n\mathbf{k}\rangle = \mathcal{N}^{-\frac{1}{2}}e^{i\mathbf{k}^*\cdot\mathbf{R}_0}e^{i(\mathbf{k}-\mathbf{k}^*)\cdot\mathbf{R}_0}, \quad (9.7)$$

so that if $\mathbf{k}$ differs from $\mathbf{k}^*$ by an amount small compared to any reciprocal lattice vector, then $\langle n\mathbf{R}_0 | n\mathbf{k}\rangle$ is equal to $e^{i\mathbf{k}^*\cdot\mathbf{R}_0}$ times a function which varies slowly on the scale of a lattice spacing. The same must then be true of the wave function of the state $|\psi\rangle$, which is assumed to be a super-position of Bloch states near $\mathbf{k} = \mathbf{k}^*$; in other words, $e^{-i\mathbf{k}^* \cdot \mathbf{R}_0}\langle n\mathbf{R}_0 \,|\, \psi\rangle$ is a slowly varying function of $\mathbf{R}_0$. In view of this fact, we can rewrite the quantity in braces in Eq. (9.6) as

$$e^{i\mathbf{k}^* \cdot \mathbf{R}_0}[e^{-i\mathbf{k}^* \cdot (\mathbf{R}_0+\mu\mathbf{a}_\sigma)}\langle n\mathbf{R}_0 + \mu\mathbf{a}_\sigma \,|\, \psi\rangle - e^{-i\mathbf{k}^* \cdot (\mathbf{R}_0-\mu\mathbf{a}_\sigma)}\langle n\mathbf{R}_0 - \mu\mathbf{a}_\sigma \,|\, \psi\rangle]$$

$$= 2e^{i\mathbf{k}^* \cdot \mathbf{R}_0}\mu\mathbf{a}_\sigma \cdot \nabla_{\mathbf{R}_0}e^{-i\mathbf{k}^* \cdot \mathbf{R}_0}\langle n\mathbf{R}_0 \,|\, \psi\rangle. \quad (9.8)$$

With this substitution and the use of Eqs. (9.2) and (8.64), Eq. (9.6) becomes

$$\langle n\mathbf{R}_0 \,|\mathscr{P}|\, \psi\rangle = \hbar\left[\mathbf{k}^* + e^{i\mathbf{k}^* \cdot \mathbf{R}_0}\frac{1}{i}\nabla_{\mathbf{R}_0}e^{-i\mathbf{k}^* \cdot \mathbf{R}_0}\right]\langle n\mathbf{R}_0 \,|\, \psi\rangle. \quad (9.9)$$

It is interesting to note that if $\mathbf{R}_0$ is formally regarded as a continuous variable, then the operator in brackets in Eq. (9.9) is identically equal to $\frac{1}{i}\nabla_{\mathbf{R}_0}$; thus as a kind of mnemonic device we can say that in the Wannier representation the dynamical variable $\mathscr{P}$ is represented by the operator

$$\mathscr{P} = \frac{\hbar}{i}\nabla_{\mathbf{R}_0}. \quad (9.10)$$

The interpretation of this rule is then the following: given a state $|\psi\rangle$, look for a vector $\mathbf{k}^*$ which makes $e^{-i\mathbf{k}^* \cdot \mathbf{R}_0}\langle n\mathbf{R}_0 \,|\, \psi\rangle$ a slowly varying function of $\mathbf{R}_0$. If such a vector exists, then the wave function of the state $\mathscr{P}|\psi\rangle$ is given by Eq. (9.9); if no such vector exists, there is no simple way of applying $\mathscr{P}$ to the wave function.

9.3 Applied Aperiodic Potential

The effective-mass approximation is concerned with the behavior of electrons in a crystal which is perturbed by an additional potential that does *not* have the periodicity of the lattice. Of course, we must assume that it does have the "large" periodicity of the boundary conditions—otherwise, the bases of the representations which we have been using cease to be complete—but this assumption has only a formal significance in applications to large crystals. Let the additional potential be denoted by $V(\mathbf{r})$; its matrix elements in the Wannier representation are then given by

$$\langle n'\mathbf{R}_0' \,|V|\, n\mathbf{R}_0\rangle = \int d^3r\,\beta_{n'}(\mathbf{r} - \mathbf{R}_0')^*V(\mathbf{r})\beta_n(\mathbf{r} - \mathbf{R}_0). \quad (9.11)$$

Suppose now that $V(\mathbf{r})$ is so slowly varying on the scale on which the β's are localized that we can neglect the error in the substitution

$$V(\mathbf{r})\beta_n(\mathbf{r} - \mathbf{R}_0) \rightarrow V(\mathbf{R}_0)\beta_n(\mathbf{r} - \mathbf{R}_0); \tag{9.12}$$

then the matrix element of V becomes

$$\langle n'\mathbf{R}_0' |V| n\mathbf{R} \rangle = V(\mathbf{R}_0)\, \delta_{\mathbf{R}_0\mathbf{R}_0'}\, \delta_{nn'}, \tag{9.13}$$

that is, the operator V in the Wannier representation is simply a multiplier $V(\mathbf{R}_0)$.

The presence of an aperiodic potential means that the crystal momentum is no longer a constant of the motion. Its rate of change is given by

$$\dot{\mathscr{P}} = \frac{i}{\hbar}\,[H, \mathscr{P}], \tag{9.14}$$

where the Hamiltonian H is

$$H = H_0 + V, \tag{9.15}$$

H_0 being the periodic crystal Hamiltonian. Since $\mathscr{P}$ and H_0 commute, we get

$$\dot{\mathscr{P}} = \frac{i}{\hbar}\,[V, \mathscr{P}]. \tag{9.16}$$

Now let $|\psi\rangle$ be a state localized in the zone; or in other words, let there exist a vector $\mathbf{k}^*$ which makes $e^{-i\mathbf{k}^* \cdot \mathbf{R}_0}\langle n\mathbf{R}_0 | \psi \rangle$ a slowly varying function of $\mathbf{R}_0$. Then, since

$$e^{-i\mathbf{k}^* \cdot \mathbf{R}_0}\langle n\mathbf{R}_0| V(\mathbf{R}_0) |\psi\rangle = V(\mathbf{R}_0)e^{-i\mathbf{k}^* \cdot \mathbf{R}_0}\langle n\mathbf{R}_0 | \psi \rangle, \tag{9.17}$$

and we have already assumed $V(\mathbf{R}_0)$ to be slowly varying, it follows that $V|\psi\rangle$ is also such a state. Therefore, from (9.16) and (9.9),

$$\langle n\mathbf{R}_0 |\mathscr{P}| \psi\rangle = V(\mathbf{R}_0)e^{i\mathbf{k}^* \cdot \mathbf{R}_0}\nabla_{\mathbf{R}_0}e^{-i\mathbf{k}^* \cdot \mathbf{R}_0}\langle n\mathbf{R}_0 | \psi \rangle$$

$$-e^{i\mathbf{k}^* \cdot \mathbf{R}_0}\nabla_{\mathbf{R}_0}e^{-i\mathbf{k}^* \cdot \mathbf{R}_0}V(\mathbf{R}_0)\langle n\mathbf{R}_0 | \psi \rangle$$

$$= \mathbf{F}(\mathbf{R}_0)\langle n\mathbf{R}_0 | \psi \rangle, \tag{9.18}$$

where

$$\mathbf{F}(\mathbf{R}_0) \equiv -\nabla_{\mathbf{R}_0} V(\mathbf{R}_0). \tag{9.19}$$

Thus as long as we treat only localized states, we may rewrite (9.18) simply as

$$\dot{\mathscr{P}} = \mathbf{F}. \tag{9.20}$$

9.4   Bloch Electron in a Constant Force Field

If the potential V represents a force $\mathbf{F}$ which is constant in space and time, Eq. (9.20) can be integrated to

$$\mathscr{P} = \mathscr{P}_0 + \mathbf{F}t. \tag{9.21}$$

This equation means that, starting at $t = 0$ with a state of definite crystal momentum, an electron would always maintain a definite value of crystal momentum, that value increasing linearly with the time. In view of the trouble we went to in Sec. 9.2 to limit the eigenvalues of $\mathscr{P}$ to a finite interval, we may well ask how that limitation can be consistent with a continuous increase of $\mathscr{P}$ at a constant rate. The fact is that the range to which we previously restricted the values of $\mathscr{P}$ depends on $\mathbf{k}^*$, the point near which the electron is localized. As $\mathscr{P}$ varies according to (9.21), we must from time to time shift to new values of $\mathbf{k}^*$. Alternatively, we may simply not worry about $\mathscr{P}$ itself and interpret Eq. (9.21) as short for

$$e^{i\mathscr{P} \cdot \mathbf{R}/\hbar} = e^{i(\mathscr{P}_0 + \mathbf{F}t) \cdot \mathbf{R}/\hbar} \tag{9.22}$$

in accordance with the spirit of Sec. 9.1. [In Eq. (9.22) $\mathbf{R}$ stands for an arbitrary lattice vector.]

As a matter of convention, we are used to regard the eigenvalue of $\mathscr{P}$ as always lying within the Brillouin zone. With this convention we may say that, under the action of a constant force, an electron moves through the zone with uniform velocity until it reaches a zone face, at which time it jumps discontinuously to that point on the opposite face which can be reached by a reciprocal lattice vector. We must not forget, however, that the "jump" actually occurs not in the electron, but in our system of labeling eigenvalues. In particular, the *wave function* of the electron experiences no discontinuous changes, since the Bloch functions are periodic in reciprocal space.

9.5   Effective-mass Schrödinger Equation

In the previous section we limited ourselves to the case where the gradient of V was constant. We now remove this restriction, and ask for solutions of the eigenvalue equation

$$H |\psi\rangle \equiv (H_0 + V) |\psi\rangle = \epsilon |\psi\rangle. \tag{9.23}$$

In effective-mass approximation, H has no interband matrix elements, so that solutions of Eq. (9.23) should exist separately for each band.

Let us choose a vector $\mathbf{k}^*$ arbitrarily and *assume* for the moment that there exist solutions of Eq. (9.23) whose wave functions in the Bloch representation are localized near $\mathbf{k}^*$. We shall then find that in fact only certain values of $\mathbf{k}^*$, which depend on the energy structure of the band, are admissible for this purpose.

If $E(\mathbf{k})$ is the energy function for the band in question, we first define a new function $E^*(\mathbf{k})$ by

$$E^*(\mathbf{k}) \equiv E(\mathbf{k} + \mathbf{k}^*). \tag{9.24}$$

The operator H_0 is then given by

$$H_0 = E(\mathscr{P}/\hbar) = E^*\left(e^{i\mathbf{k}^* \cdot \mathbf{R}_0} \frac{1}{i} \nabla_{\mathbf{R}_0} e^{-i\mathbf{k}^* \cdot \mathbf{R}_0}\right), \tag{9.25}$$

where Eqs. (9.24) and (9.9) have been used. Assuming that E^* has a power series expansion, we obtain

$$H_0 = e^{i\mathbf{k}^* \cdot \mathbf{R}_0} E^*\left(\frac{1}{i} \nabla_{\mathbf{R}_0}\right) e^{-i\mathbf{k}^* \cdot \mathbf{R}_0}; \tag{9.26}$$

Eq. (9.23) in the Wannier representation is then

$$e^{i\mathbf{k}^* \cdot \mathbf{R}_0} E^*\left(\frac{1}{i} \nabla_{\mathbf{R}_0}\right) e^{-i\mathbf{k}^* \cdot \mathbf{R}_0} \langle \mathbf{R}_0 \mid \psi \rangle + V(\mathbf{R}_0)\langle \mathbf{R}_0 \mid \psi \rangle = \epsilon \langle \mathbf{R}_0 \mid \psi \rangle, \tag{9.27}$$

or

$$\left[E^*\left(\frac{1}{i} \nabla_{\mathbf{R}_0}\right) + V(\mathbf{R}_0) - \epsilon\right]\Psi(\mathbf{R}_0) = 0, \tag{9.28}$$

where

$$\Psi(\mathbf{R}_0) \equiv e^{-i\mathbf{k}^* \cdot \mathbf{R}_0}\langle \mathbf{R}_0 \mid \psi \rangle. \tag{9.29}$$

Since $\Psi(\mathbf{R}_0)$ is precisely the function which, according to Sec. 9.2, must be slowly varying in order for the representation (9.9) to apply, we are led to ask under what conditions Eq. (9.28) has solutions which are slow functions of $\mathbf{R}_0$. To answer this question, which is a purely mathematical one, we first note that no such solutions can in general be expected unless the coefficient $V(\mathbf{R}_0)$ is itself slowly varying. This is, however, not a new restriction, since if V varied rapidly the substitution (9.12) could not have been made in the first place.

A new condition has, however, to be imposed on the function E^*. Let Eq. (9.28) be transformed by a Fourier integral; the requirement on Ψ is then that its Fourier transform must be localized near zero. This can happen only if E^*, which acts as a potential in the transformed space, has a minimum when its argument is zero. Therefore, *meaningful solutions of the effective-mass Schrödinger equation cannot be found unless* V *is a slowly varying function and* $\mathbf{k}^*$ *is chosen at a point where* E(k) *is a minimum.*

These two conditions are still not sufficient, however; for as we know by analogy with the ordinary Schrödinger equation, Eq. (9.28) will have solutions with higher and higher eigenvalues ϵ which vary more and more rapidly with $\mathbf{R}_0$; therefore at best only a limited number of low-lying states can be found by this approach.

Since $E(\mathbf{k})$ must be a minimum at $\mathbf{k} = \mathbf{k}^*$, the expansion of $E^*(\mathbf{k})$ in a Maclaurin series will lack a linear term, so that

$$E^*(\mathbf{k}) = E_0^* + \frac{1}{2} \sum_{\alpha\beta} \mu_{\alpha\beta} k_\alpha k_\beta + \cdots \qquad (9.30)$$

where

$$\mu_{\alpha\beta} \equiv \frac{\partial^2 E^*(0)}{\partial k_\alpha \partial k_\beta}. \qquad (9.31)$$

Terms in E^* of degrees higher than quadratic can usually be neglected, since the solution to Eq. (9.28) must be highly localized in reciprocal space. By appropriately choosing the coordinate system, $\mu_{\alpha\beta}$ can be made to contain only diagonal terms, which are usually written as

$$\mu_{11} \equiv \frac{\hbar^2}{m_1^*}, \quad \mu_{22} \equiv \frac{\hbar^2}{m_2^*}, \quad \mu_{33} \equiv \frac{\hbar^2}{m_3^*}. \qquad (9.32)$$

The m^*'s are called the *principal effective masses* at the point $\mathbf{k}^*$. If we further agree to consider E_0^* as the zero of energy, Eq. (9.28) becomes

$$\left[-\frac{\hbar^2}{2m_1^*} \frac{\partial^2}{\partial X^2} - \frac{\hbar^2}{2m_2^*} \frac{\partial^2}{\partial Y^2} - \frac{\hbar^2}{2m_3^*} \frac{\partial^2}{\partial Z^2} + V(\mathbf{R}_0) - \epsilon \right] \Psi(\mathbf{R}_0) = 0, \qquad (9.33)$$

where X, Y, Z are the components of $\mathbf{R}_0$ in the directions 1, 2, 3 which diagonalize the effective-mass tensor. Equation (9.33) looks like the ordinary Schrödinger equation for a particle in a potential V, except that the inertial properties of the particle are anisotropic.

9.6   Kohn-Luttinger Representation

An alternative starting point for effective-mass theory is obtained by using a representation similar to, but not the same as, the Bloch representation. The basis functions are taken to be

$$\varphi_{n\mathbf{k}}(\mathbf{r}) \equiv u_{n\mathbf{k}*}(\mathbf{r}) e^{i\mathbf{k} \cdot \mathbf{r}}; \qquad (9.34)$$

they have the form of Bloch functions, except that the periodic part is always the periodic part of the Bloch function of a *particular* crystal momentum $\mathbf{k}^*$, so that the dependence of $\varphi_{n\mathbf{k}}$ upon $\mathbf{k}$ lies entirely in the plane-wave exponential. It is proved in Problem 1 that the "Kohn-Luttinger functions" (9.34) do indeed comprise a complete orthogonal set.

To investigate the properties of the new representation, let us first write the Hamiltonian matrix. Starting with

$$H\varphi_{n\mathbf{k}}(\mathbf{r}) = \left[\frac{p^2}{2m} + U(\mathbf{r})\right] u_{n\mathbf{k}*}(\mathbf{r})e^{i\mathbf{k}\cdot\mathbf{r}}$$

$$= e^{i\mathbf{k}\cdot\mathbf{r}}\left[-\frac{\hbar^2}{2m}(\nabla + i\mathbf{k})^2 + U(\mathbf{r})\right] u_{n\mathbf{k}*}(\mathbf{r}), \qquad (9.35)$$

we first eliminate the potential U; this is easily done, since $u_{n\mathbf{k}*}$ satisfies Eq. (6.7) with $\mathbf{k} = \mathbf{k}^*$. We thus obtain

$$H\varphi_{n\mathbf{k}}(\mathbf{r})$$

$$= e^{i\mathbf{k}\cdot\mathbf{r}}\left[-\frac{\hbar^2}{2m}(\nabla + i\mathbf{k})^2 + E_n(\mathbf{k}^*) + \frac{\hbar^2}{2m}(\nabla + i\mathbf{k}^*)^2\right] u_{n\mathbf{k}*}(\mathbf{r})$$

$$= e^{i\mathbf{k}\cdot\mathbf{r}}\left[E_n(\mathbf{k}^*) + \frac{\hbar^2}{2m}(\mathbf{k} - \mathbf{k}^*)^2 + \hbar(\mathbf{k} - \mathbf{k}^*)\cdot\frac{\hbar}{im}(\nabla + i\mathbf{k}^*)\right] u_{n\mathbf{k}*}(\mathbf{r}).$$
$$(9.36)$$

Accordingly, the matrix of H in the Kohn-Luttinger representation is

$$(n'\mathbf{k}'|\, H\, |n\mathbf{k}) = \delta_{\mathbf{k}\mathbf{k}'}\left[E_n(\mathbf{k}^*)\,\delta_{nn'} + \frac{\hbar^2}{2m}(\mathbf{k} - \mathbf{k}^*)^2\,\delta_{nn'}\right.$$

$$\left. + \hbar(\mathbf{k} - \mathbf{k}^*)\cdot\langle n'\mathbf{k}^*|\,\mathbf{v}\,|n\mathbf{k}^*\rangle\right]; \quad (9.37)$$

note that we use bra and ket vectors with parentheses ( ) to distinguish the Kohn-Luttinger basis from the Bloch basis $|n\mathbf{k}\rangle$. The matrix $\langle n'\mathbf{k}^*|\,\mathbf{v}\,|n\mathbf{k}^*\rangle$ is simply the interband matrix of the operator $\mathbf{p}/m$ in the Bloch representation, evaluated between states of crystal momentum $\mathbf{k}^*$.[3]

Since Eq. (9.37) is diagonal in $\mathbf{k}$, it is useful to view its terms as being matrices in *band space* which depend parametrically on $\mathbf{k}$. The appropriate notation is then

$$H = E(\mathbf{k}^*) + \frac{\hbar^2}{2m}(\mathbf{k} - \mathbf{k}^*)^2 + \hbar(\mathbf{k} - \mathbf{k}^*)\cdot\mathbf{v}(\mathbf{k}^*), \qquad (9.38)$$

where $E(\mathbf{k})$ is the diagonal matrix whose elements are $E_n(\mathbf{k})$, $\mathbf{v}(\mathbf{k})$ is the matrix $\langle n'\mathbf{k}|\,\mathbf{v}\,|n\mathbf{k}\rangle$, and the middle term is to be understood as containing the unit matrix as a factor.

---

[3] The momentum $\mathbf{p}$ commutes with the crystal momentum and therefore has no matrix elements between states of different $\mathbf{k}$ (cf. Problem 2).

At the point $\mathbf{k} = \mathbf{k}^*$, the Kohn-Luttinger Hamiltonian has, of course, only the diagonal elements $E_n(\mathbf{k}^*)$. For nearby points in the zone, the terms containing $\mathbf{k} - \mathbf{k}^*$ can be treated as a perturbation. In particular, if $\mathbf{k}^*$ represents a point of minimum energy for the band n, then the diagonal element $\mathbf{v}(\mathbf{k}^*)_{nn}$ vanishes; we then obtain, to second order in $\mathbf{k} - \mathbf{k}^*$,

$$E_n(\mathbf{k}) = E_n(\mathbf{k}^*)$$

$$+ \frac{\hbar^2}{2} (\mathbf{k} - \mathbf{k}^*) \cdot \left[\frac{1}{m} \mathbf{I} + 2 \sum_{n' \neq n} \frac{\mathbf{v}(\mathbf{k}^*)_{nn'} \mathbf{v}(\mathbf{k}^*)_{n'n}}{E_n(\mathbf{k}^*) - E_{n'}(\mathbf{k}^*)} \right] \cdot (\mathbf{k} - \mathbf{k}^*). \quad (9.39)$$

When compared with Eq. (9.30), the expression in brackets gives a useful formula for the effective-mass tensor in terms of interband matrix elements of $\mathbf{v}$.

9.7 Applied Potential in Kohn-Luttinger Representation

Suppose we have a state $|\psi\rangle$ whose wave function in the Kohn-Luttinger representation is $(n\mathbf{k} \mid \psi)$. Then the wave function of the state $\mathbf{r} \mid \psi\rangle$ is

$$(n\mathbf{k}| \, \mathbf{r} \, |\psi\rangle = \sum_{\mathbf{r}'} (n\mathbf{k} \mid \mathbf{r}')\langle \mathbf{r}'| \, \mathbf{r} \, |\psi\rangle = \sum_{\mathbf{r}'} (n\mathbf{k} \mid \mathbf{r}')\mathbf{r}'\langle \mathbf{r}' \mid \psi\rangle. \quad (9.40)$$

But from Eq. (9.34) we have[4]

$$(n\mathbf{k} \mid \mathbf{r}') = u_{n\mathbf{k}*}(\mathbf{r}')^* e^{-i\mathbf{k} \cdot \mathbf{r}'}, \quad (9.41)$$

so that

$$(n\mathbf{k} \mid \mathbf{r}')\mathbf{r}' = i\nabla_{\mathbf{k}}(n\mathbf{k} \mid \mathbf{r}'); \quad (9.42)$$

therefore

$$(n\mathbf{k}| \, \mathbf{r} \, |\psi\rangle = i\nabla_{\mathbf{k}} \sum_{\mathbf{r}'} (n\mathbf{k} \mid \mathbf{r}')\langle \mathbf{r}' \mid \psi\rangle = i\nabla_{\mathbf{k}}(n\mathbf{k} \mid \psi). \quad (9.43)$$

Thus the operator $i\nabla_{\mathbf{k}}$, which in the Bloch representation stands for $\mathbf{R}$, represents the continuous variable $\mathbf{r}$ in the Kohn-Luttinger representation. It is this fact which makes the new representation convenient as the starting point of effective-mass theory.

Suppose we consider the problem of Sec. 9.3. The Hamiltonian matrix including the applied potential is

$$H = E(\mathbf{k}^*) + \frac{\hbar^2}{2m} (\mathbf{k} - \mathbf{k}^*)^2 + \mathbf{v}(\mathbf{k}^*) \cdot \hbar(\mathbf{k} - \mathbf{k}^*) + V(i\nabla_{\mathbf{k}}); \quad (9.44)$$

---

[4] The function $\varphi_{n\mathbf{k}}(\mathbf{r})$ given by Eq. (9.34) is the wave function of the state $|n\mathbf{k})$ in the $\mathbf{r}$-representation, i.e., $\langle \mathbf{r} \mid n\mathbf{k} \rangle$.

the last term is a constant so far as the band index n is concerned. Now we generally assume that if a matrix is a constant (i.e., a multiple of the unit matrix) in a certain space, then it will be unchanged by any similarity transformation in that space. Thus we might be led to conclude that since there exists a diagonalizing transformation[5] which changes the first three terms of (9.44) into $E(\mathbf{k})$, the same transformation will bring the total Hamiltonian into the form

$$H = E(\mathbf{k}) + V(i\nabla_{\mathbf{k}}) \tag{9.45}$$

in which *both* terms are diagonal in the bands. Such a conclusion is, of course, quite wrong, since it would imply that no applied potential ever has any matrix elements between different bands of the unperturbed crystal.

The fallacy, as the reader has probably realized, is that the similarity transformation which diagonalizes the unperturbed Hamiltonian depends on $\mathbf{k}$, and therefore does not commute with $V(i\nabla_{\mathbf{k}})$. In other words, $\mathbf{k}$ is no longer a constant of the motion, so that we can no longer assign a numerical value to it and diagonalize afterwards. In fact, the rate of change of $\mathbf{k}$ is given by

$$\dot{\mathbf{k}} = \frac{i}{\hbar}[V(i\nabla_{\mathbf{k}}), \mathbf{k}] = \frac{1}{\hbar}\mathbf{F}(i\nabla_{\mathbf{k}}), \tag{9.46}$$

where $\mathbf{F}$ is the negative gradient of V with respect to its argument, that is, the applied force. This equation is the same as (9.20), but we have obtained it this time without making any approximations.

To estimate the interband matrix elements of V, we note that the unitary transformation which diagonalizes the first three terms of (9.44) is, to first order in $\mathbf{k} - \mathbf{k}^*$,

$$S_{nn'}(\mathbf{k}) = \delta_{nn'} + \frac{\mathbf{v}(\mathbf{k}^*)_{nn'}}{E_n(\mathbf{k}^*) - E_{n'}(\mathbf{k}^*)} \cdot \hbar(\mathbf{k} - \mathbf{k}^*). \tag{9.47}$$

Applying this transformation to V, we obtain

$$S(\mathbf{k})V(i\nabla_{\mathbf{k}})S^{-1}(\mathbf{k}) = V(i\nabla_{\mathbf{k}}) + \frac{\mathbf{v}(\mathbf{k}^*)_{nn'}}{E_n(\mathbf{k}^*) - E_{n'}(\mathbf{k}^*)} \cdot [V(i\nabla_{\mathbf{k}}), \hbar(\mathbf{k} - \mathbf{k}^*)]$$

$$= V(i\nabla_{\mathbf{k}}) + \frac{\mathbf{v}(\mathbf{k}^*)_{nn'} \cdot \hbar\mathbf{F}(i\nabla_{\mathbf{k}})}{E_n(\mathbf{k}^*) - E_{n'}(\mathbf{k}^*)}. \tag{9.48}$$

[5] That is, the transformation from the Kohn-Luttinger representation to the Bloch representation.

The second term gives the interband matrix elements of the perturbation (v has no diagonal elements since k* is assumed to be at a minimum). The Hamiltonian, after this transformation, becomes

$$H = E(\mathbf{k}) + V(i\nabla_\mathbf{k}) + \text{off-diagonal elements linear in } \mathbf{F}. \qquad (9.49)$$

We can now visualize a further transformation which would eliminate the off-diagonal elements, and perturbation theory tells us that off-diagonal elements linear in **F** will give rise to diagonal elements at least quadratic in **F**. We conclude that *the Hamiltonian*

$$H = E(\mathbf{k}) + V(i\nabla_\mathbf{k}) \qquad (9.50)$$

is correct for forces which are sufficiently weak and sufficiently slowly varying. The requirement of slow variation comes from the fact that in using the first-order formula (9.47) we are tacitly assuming that V will only connect values of **k** which are close together in the zone.

9.8   Kohn-Luttinger Schrödinger Equation

The eigenvalues and eigenfunctions of the Hamiltonian (9.50) are determined by the equation

$$[E(\mathbf{k}) + V(i\nabla_\mathbf{k}) - \epsilon]\Phi(\mathbf{k}) = 0, \qquad (9.51)$$

$\Phi(\mathbf{k})$ being the wave function of the energy eigenstate in the Kohn-Luttinger representation. Since we are considering the bands to be decoupled, we may replace $E(\mathbf{k})$ by $E_n(\mathbf{k})$, n being the particular band out of which we are trying to construct eigenstates of H. A Fourier integral transformation applied to Eq. (9.51) yields

$$\left[E^*\left(\frac{1}{i}\nabla\right) + V(\bar{\mathbf{r}}) - \epsilon\right]F(\bar{\mathbf{r}}) = 0, \qquad (9.52)$$

where F is given by

$$F(\bar{\mathbf{r}}) \equiv \int \Phi(\mathbf{k})e^{i(\mathbf{k}-\mathbf{k}^*)\cdot\bar{\mathbf{r}}} d^3k, \qquad (9.53)$$

∇ stands for the gradient with respect to the new variable $\bar{\mathbf{r}}$, and E^* is defined by Eq. (9.24). The surface integrals which appear in transforming from (9.51) to (9.52) are omitted on the basis of the assumption that $\Phi(\mathbf{k})$ vanishes except in a relatively small region $\mathbf{k} \approx \mathbf{k}^*$; by the same token, the exact domain of integration in **k**-space is unimportant, so long as it is large enough to include the region where Φ is different from zero. Equation (9.52) has exactly the same form as Eq. (9.28) which was derived via the

Wannier representation, so that the eigenvalues ϵ will be the same. Let us now compare the eigenfunctions. We can obtain $\Phi(\mathbf{k})$ from $F(\bar{\mathbf{r}})$ by the inverse of (9.53):

$$\Phi(\mathbf{k}) = (2\pi)^{-3} \int F(\bar{\mathbf{r}}) e^{-i(\mathbf{k}-\mathbf{k}^*)\cdot\bar{\mathbf{r}}} \, d^3\bar{r}; \tag{9.54}$$

the wave function in $\mathbf{r}$-representation is then

$$\psi(\mathbf{r}) \equiv \int d^3k \, \langle \mathbf{r} \mid n\mathbf{k}\rangle \Phi(\mathbf{k})$$

$$= (2\pi)^{-3} \int d^3k \, d^3\bar{r} \, u_{n\mathbf{k}*}(\mathbf{r}) e^{i\mathbf{k}\cdot\mathbf{r}} F(\bar{\mathbf{r}}) e^{-i(\mathbf{k}-\mathbf{k}^*)\cdot\bar{\mathbf{r}}}$$

$$= F(\mathbf{r}) u_{n\mathbf{k}*}(\mathbf{r}) e^{i\mathbf{k}^*\cdot\mathbf{r}}. \tag{9.55}$$

Thus $F(\mathbf{r})$ has a simple physical significance: it is an *envelope function* by which the Bloch function corresponding to the point $\mathbf{k}^*$ has to be multiplied to yield the eigenfunction of the perturbed Hamiltonian. On the other hand, the eigenfunction $\Psi(\mathbf{R}_0)$ determined in Sec. 9.5 from a formally identical equation was in fact, according to (9.29), the wave function in the Wannier representation multiplied by $\exp(-i\mathbf{k}^*\cdot\mathbf{R}_0)$. Transforming from Wannier representation to $\mathbf{r}$-representation yields

$$\psi(\mathbf{r}) = \sum_{\mathbf{R}_0} \langle \mathbf{r} \mid n\mathbf{R}_0\rangle \Psi(\mathbf{R}_0) e^{i\mathbf{k}^*\cdot\mathbf{R}_0}. \tag{9.56}$$

Now $\langle \mathbf{r} \mid n\mathbf{R}_0\rangle$ is the Wannier function $\beta_n(\mathbf{r} - \mathbf{R}_0)$ which, as we have seen, is strongly localized near $\mathbf{r} = \mathbf{R}_0$; whereas $\Psi(\mathbf{R}_0)$ must be a slowly varying function of $\mathbf{R}_0$ for effective-mass theory to apply. Therefore no *new* error is introduced by making the substitution

$$\langle \mathbf{r} \mid n\mathbf{R}_0\rangle \Psi(\mathbf{R}_0) \rightarrow \langle \mathbf{r} \mid n\mathbf{R}_0\rangle \Psi(\mathbf{r}); \tag{9.57}$$

Eq. (9.56) then becomes

$$\psi(\mathbf{r}) = \Psi(\mathbf{r}) \sum_{\mathbf{R}_0} \langle \mathbf{r} \mid n\mathbf{R}_0\rangle e^{i\mathbf{k}^*\cdot\mathbf{R}_0}$$

$$= \mathcal{N}^{1/2}\Psi(\mathbf{r}) \sum_{\mathbf{R}_0} \langle \mathbf{r} \mid n\mathbf{R}_0\rangle\langle n\mathbf{R}_0 \mid n\mathbf{k}^*\rangle$$

$$= \mathcal{N}^{1/2}\Psi(\mathbf{r})\langle \mathbf{r} \mid n\mathbf{k}^*\rangle$$

$$= \mathcal{N}^{1/2}\Psi(\mathbf{r}) u_{n\mathbf{k}*}(\mathbf{r}) e^{i\mathbf{k}^*\cdot\mathbf{r}}. \tag{9.58}$$

This result is the same as Eq. (9.55), except for the factor of $\mathcal{N}^{1/2}$ which arises from a trivial difference in normalization conventions. We therefore conclude that *the Kohn-Luttinger effective-mass theory is equivalent to the Wannier theory provided that the criteria for the applicability of effective-mass theory are satisfied in the first place.*

9.9 Example: Donor States in Germanium

As was mentioned in Sec. 7.8, a pentavalent impurity introduced substitutionally into the germanium lattice gives rise to localized electron states whose energies are lower than the minimum energy of the conduction band. In the present section we shall discuss the origin of such states.

The added potential due to the donor ion is

$$V = -e^2/Kr. \tag{9.59}$$

The dielectric constant K, which arises from polarization of the *full valence band* by the field of the ion, is introduced here in a purely phenomenological way.

Before applying effective-mass theory, we must determine the admissible values of $\mathbf{k}^*$. The Bravais lattice of germanium is face-centered cubic, so that its Brillouin zone has the shape shown in Fig. 2.6. It turns out that the conduction band has four absolute minima at the centers of the hexagonal faces of the zone (there are, of course, *eight* hexagonal faces, but points on the surface of a zone are always equivalent in pairs). In addition, there is a relative minimum on each of the six lines connecting the origin of the zone to the centers of the square faces, and also a single relative minimum at the origin itself. Thus we have a total of eleven points at which we can center the effective mass equations.

Let us first examine the choice $\mathbf{k}^* = 0$. Because the crystal has cubic symmetry, the three effective masses in Eq. (9.33) must be equal, so that they can be denoted by the single symbol m^*. The equation then becomes

$$-\frac{\hbar^2}{2m^*}\nabla^2\Psi - \frac{e^2}{KR_0}\Psi = \epsilon\Psi, \tag{9.60}$$

which we recognize as being identical to the ordinary hydrogen atom equation, except for the numerical substitutions $m \to m^*$ and $e^2 \to e^2/K$. Thus the eigenvalues ϵ are immediately given by the modified Balmer formula

$$\epsilon_n = -\frac{m^*e^4}{2K^2\hbar^2n^2}, \qquad n = 1, 2, 3, \ldots. \tag{9.61}$$

The validity of the solutions depends on whether they do, indeed, vary slowly on the scale of a lattice spacing. The modified Bohr radius corresponding to Eq. (9.60) is

$$a_B = \frac{\hbar^2K}{m^*e^2}, \tag{9.62}$$

so that the solutions are valid provided

$$\frac{\hbar^2 K}{m^* e^2} \gg a \tag{9.63}$$

where a is a lattice spacing. It turns out that for germanium this condition is fairly well satisfied.

The lowest state of Eq. (9.61), for which $n = 1$, has a "binding energy" $-\epsilon_1$ of the order of a hundredth of an electron-volt, which is less (by about a factor of ten) than the energy by which the relative minimum of $E(\mathbf{k})$ at $\mathbf{k} = 0$ is higher than the absolute minima on the hexagonal faces of the zone, so that the choice $\mathbf{k}^* = 0$ does not give energy levels in the forbidden gap. Clearly, we should start with $\mathbf{k}^*$ at one of the absolute minima. Here the group of the wave vector includes a threefold axis perpendicular to the zone face, so that if we choose the Z-axis in this direction, we can write

$$m_1^* = m_2^* \equiv m_\perp, \tag{9.64}$$

$$m_3^* \equiv m_\parallel, \tag{9.65}$$

as a result of which Eq. (9.33) becomes

$$\left\{ -\frac{\hbar^2}{2m_\perp}\left(\frac{\partial^2}{\partial X^2} + \frac{\partial^2}{\partial Y^2}\right) - \frac{\hbar^2}{2m_\parallel}\frac{\partial^2}{\partial Z^2} - \frac{e^2}{KR_0} \right\} \Psi = \epsilon \Psi. \tag{9.66}$$

Equation (9.66) is mathematically considerably more troublesome than (9.60) since it is not separable, and solutions cannot be found in closed form; but this is no more than a computational difficulty. Approximate solutions to (9.66) have been obtained by various methods and the agreement with experimental data on donor states in the forbidden gap is, by and large, good.

9.10 Motion in a Magnetic Field

In the presence of a magnetic field, the one-electron Hamiltonian is

$$H = \frac{1}{2m}\left(\mathbf{p} - \frac{e}{c}\mathbf{A}\right)^2 + U(\mathbf{r}), \tag{9.67}$$

$\mathbf{A}$ being the vector potential. We note immediately that for a uniform field $\mathbf{A}$ can never be treated as a small perturbation, since it increases linearly with distance and will therefore be very large in some regions of the crystal.

Putting the Hamiltonian (9.67) into the Kohn-Luttinger representation in analogy with Eqs. (9.36) to (9.38), we obtain the matrix

$$H = E(\mathbf{k}^*) + \frac{\hbar^2}{2m}\left[\mathbf{k} - \mathbf{k}^* - \frac{e}{\hbar c}\mathbf{A}(i\nabla_\mathbf{k})\right]^2$$

$$+ \mathbf{v}(\mathbf{k}^*) \cdot \hbar\left[\mathbf{k} - \mathbf{k}^* - \frac{e}{\hbar c}\mathbf{A}(i\nabla_\mathbf{k})\right]$$

$$= E(\mathbf{k}^*) + \frac{\hbar^2}{2m}(\varkappa - \mathbf{k}^*)^2 + \mathbf{v}(\mathbf{k}^*) \cdot \hbar(\varkappa - \mathbf{k}^*), \qquad (9.68)$$

where
$$\varkappa \equiv \mathbf{k} - \frac{e}{\hbar c}\mathbf{A}; \qquad (9.69)$$

in other words, the Hamiltonian is obtained from the unperturbed Hamiltonian by replacing $\mathbf{k}$ with $\varkappa$. Now the three operators which form the components of the vector operator $\varkappa$ each have a continuous range of eigenvalues, so that we might think of assigning a numerical value to each of them and then diagonalizing H. Since the diagonalizing transformation would be the same as the one to be used on (9.38) with the corresponding values of the components of $\mathbf{k}$, the result ought to be simply

$$H = E(\varkappa). \qquad (9.70)$$

Equation (9.70) is not correct because of a difficulty which is similar to, but rather more severe than, the one encountered in Sec. 9.7. We were troubled there by the fact that $\mathbf{k}$ did not commute with H, so that after assigning numerical values to k_x, k_y, and k_z we could no longer diagonalize the Hamiltonian. In the present case the question of whether the Hamiltonian commutes with $\varkappa$ never arises, because *the different components of $\varkappa$ do not commute with each other.* In particular, we have

$$[\varkappa_x, \varkappa_y] = \left[k_x - \frac{e}{\hbar c}A_x(i\nabla_\mathbf{k}), k_y - \frac{e}{\hbar c}A_y(i\nabla_\mathbf{k})\right] = \frac{ie}{\hbar c}B_z(i\nabla_\mathbf{k}), \quad (9.71)$$

$\mathbf{B}$ being the magnetic field; or, in somewhat symbolic notation,

$$\varkappa \times \varkappa = \frac{ie}{\hbar c}\mathbf{B}. \qquad (9.72)$$

Thus there exist no simultaneous eigenfunctions of the three components of $\varkappa$, so that we cannot assign numerical values to them, completely apart from diagonalizing the Hamiltonian at the same time.

On the other hand, the noncommutativity of the components of $\varkappa$ is, according to Eq. (9.72), measured by the magnitude of $\mathbf{B}$, not $\mathbf{A}$, so that a perturbation treatment in powers of $\mathbf{B}$ should be possible. In particular, if a transformation were made to decouple the bands, the resulting Hamiltonian matrix would be diagonal in the new bands, with matrix elements $F_n(\varkappa)$ which are functions of $\varkappa$; these functions could then be expanded in a power series in $\mathbf{B}$, of which $E_n(\varkappa)$ would be the zero-order term.

If, for example, we are dealing with electrons near a band minimum, for which

$$E_n(\varkappa) = \frac{1}{2} \sum_{\alpha\beta} \mu_{\alpha\beta} \varkappa_\alpha \varkappa_\beta, \tag{9.73}$$

then Eq. (9.73) may be regarded as a zero-order approximation to the Hamiltonian. If the effective-mass tensor is isotropic, (9.73) reduces to the familiar Hamiltonian of a free particle of mass m^* in a magnetic field; the interesting situation of an anisotropic mass is developed in Problem 4 at the end of this chapter.

9.11   The Lorentz Force

Using the commutation rule (9.72) along with the obvious one

$$[\mathbf{k}, \mathbf{r}] = [\mathbf{k}, i\nabla_\mathbf{k}] = -i\mathbf{I} \tag{9.74}$$

(**I** being the unit dyadic), we find the velocity operator corresponding to (9.68) to be

$$\dot{\mathbf{r}} \equiv \frac{i}{\hbar} [H, i\nabla_\mathbf{k}] = \frac{\hbar}{m} (\varkappa - \mathbf{k}^*) + \mathbf{v}, \tag{9.75}$$

whereas the rate of change of $\varkappa$ turns out to be given by

$$\dot{\varkappa} = \frac{i}{\hbar} [H, \varkappa] = \frac{e}{2\hbar c} \left\{ \left[\frac{\hbar}{m} (\varkappa - \mathbf{k}^*) + \mathbf{v} \right] \times \mathbf{B} \right.$$

$$\left. - \mathbf{B} \times \left[\frac{\hbar}{m} (\varkappa - \mathbf{k}^*) + \mathbf{v} \right] \right\}. \tag{9.76}$$

We may therefore write

$$\hbar\dot{\varkappa} = \frac{e}{2c} (\dot{\mathbf{r}} \times \mathbf{B} - \mathbf{B} \times \dot{\mathbf{r}}), \tag{9.77}$$

which has the familiar appearance of the Lorentz force.[6] Equation (9.77) indicates that $\hbar\varkappa$ is to be regarded as the "kinetic crystal momentum"; that is, its three noncommuting components are the coordinates of the electron in the Brillouin zone. It is important to realize how drastic is the

---

[6] The symmetrization of the cross-product is unnecessary if **B** does not depend on position, since it then commutes with $\varkappa$ and hence with $\dot{\mathbf{r}}$.

effect which this interpretation has on the concept of band structure. When we dealt with electrostatic potentials only, we could still ask questions such as: "given the exact position of an electron in the zone at time zero, what will be the probability of finding it at some other point at some later time?" As soon as a magnetic field is introduced, it becomes impossible to give even initial values to all three zone coordinates; just as it is impossible to specify position and momentum of an electron simultaneously, quite apart from what the laws of motion may be.

PROBLEMS

1. Prove that the Kohn-Luttinger functions, Eq. (9.34), comprise a complete orthogonal set.

2. Prove that the crystal momentum commutes with the ordinary momentum.

3. If we let $m_{\parallel} \to \infty$, Eq. (9.66) is satisfied by solutions of the form $\Psi(X, Y, Z) = \Phi(X, Y)\delta(Z)$. Find the energy spectrum of the corresponding "two-dimensional" hydrogen atom.

4. Find the energy levels of the Hamiltonian (9.73) in the case of a uniform magnetic field. Let **B** be in the z-direction, and choose the x and y axes so that $\mu_{xy} = 0$.

Index